RELIGION AND
BIRTH CONTROL

by John Clover Monsma

THE SHEPHERD KING

THE STORY OF THE CHURCH

AMERICAN FUNDAMENTALS

Edited by John Clover Monsma

THIS I BELIEVE ABOUT JESUS CHRIST

THE EVIDENCE OF GOD IN AN EXPANDING
   UNIVERSE

SCIENCE AND RELIGION

RELIGION AND BIRTH CONTROL

RELIGION AND
BIRTH CONTROL

TWENTY-ONE MEDICAL SPECIALISTS
WRITE IN PLAIN LANGUAGE ABOUT—

Control of Conception

Therapeutic Abortion

Sterilization

Natural Childbirth

Artificial Insemination

EDITED BY

JOHN CLOVER MONSMA

DOUBLEDAY & COMPANY, INC.
GARDEN CITY, NEW YORK, 1963

Library of Congress Catalog Card Number 63–12988
Copyright © 1963 by John Clover Monsma
All Rights Reserved
Printed in the United States of America
First Edition

ACKNOWLEDGMENT

We are deeply grateful to the fine group of medical specialists who consented to join us in the preparation of this volume. Doctors are, proverbially, very busy men. When in all their incessant, rushing activity they force themselves to a halt, give themselves to study and cogitation, and then note down or dictate the gist of their thoughts—that simply means that they consider the subject in hand of transcendent importance. We are glad that we found the courage to invite them to collaborate. The invitations never could have been accepted with finer grace.

J.C.M.

CONTENTS

Part III   STERILIZATION

Part IV   NATURAL CHILDBIRTH

Part V. ARTIFICIAL INSEMINATION

EDITOR'S INTRODUCTION

A large number of young married people lead lives of suppressed anxiety. They have a disturbed conscience, and their minds, as a consequence, fight an interminable series of hushed inner battles.

The trouble is due to problems connected with sex and the procreative process. In cases where religion is taken very seriously consciences are especially sensitized and anxiety is increased. Consultation with the doctor may help, and then again it may not. Doctors are educated, trained, and ordinarily very dependable advisers in things medical, but not all doctors are sufficiently equipped to deal with confidential problems of a religio-ethical nature. In fact, many physicians have told me that when they come to face such problems among their patients they are frequently pretty much at sea.

This troublesome situation has developed largely in our modern age. As is well known, in natural science more progress has been made during the past half century than in many previous centuries combined. Medical science has kept pace. There are new diagnostic procedures, new and highly delicate operations, modern techniques of every sort that nineteenth-century doctors never dreamed of, instruments of unbelievably fine and complicated workmanship, countless and oftentimes highly rewarding clinical investigations, specialization in every branch and offshoot of medicine, and a great variety of new drugs for internal and external use.

All this vast progress has had a decided effect on human sex life and procreation, particularly in Western countries. Men and women in their marital relationship have been provided with new means and methods that in the estimation of many spell greater freedom and deeper satisfaction. They have acquired a sense of mastery over themselves and over certain spoilsport, irksome natural laws that held humanity chained since time began—or so, at least, they feel about it.

The trouble is that not all feel at liberty to make use, unquestioningly, of these new means and methods. Many people, especially many church-connected people, have moral scruples. In fact, the number is very large of those who either firmly or falteringly reject the new sex apparatus and certain modern practices connected with procreation. Others accept both, but unless the problem of conscience is solved, anxiety may be increased. What all those people have needed for a long time is light on their situation and guidance in their confused, battle-weary inner lives.

In publishing this book we seek to shed some of that light and furnish some of that guidance. Twenty-one doctors have been invited to discuss a variety of subjects related to procreation. They are specialists in andriatrics (disorders peculiar to men), gynecology (science of diseases of women), and obstetrics. Among them are professors of medicine, heads of clinics and hospital departments, and capable practicing physicians. And what we wish to stress particularly is that all the writers in this volume are men who recognize and honor the spiritual nature of man and thus are furnished to meet the requirements predicated in our general title—*Religion and Birth Control.*

The book, as will have been noted, is divided into five sections, each with its own subhead. Several doctors discuss the same material under each subhead. They write independently, each in his own way, and thus light is shed on the same subject from different angles, and the readers will be enabled, through quiet reflection and the leading of conscience, to reach a fixed and satisfying conclusion for themselves.

In mentioning "reflection" and "conscience," just now, we suddenly arrived at the fountainhead of all the personal and ethical questions that pertain to sex and reproduction. They go together and are inseparable—reflection and conscience. Many people mistakenly think of conscience as a function of the emotional part of their being, of the "heart." Actually it is a function of the intellect, the reflecting mind, though emotions, too, are liable to play a role.

Right here our readers may appreciate a few additional explanatory remarks. We use the word "religion" in the book's title. That word has been derived from the Latin *religare,* which means "to bind together again," namely God and man, after the rebellion and rupture of sin. Our English words "ligament" and "ligature" are from the same root, and both signify something that binds or ties together. Another English word that has come to us from *religare,* and that has a derivative meaning, is the word "rely" or "rely upon." The verbal similarity of "religion" and "rely" is apparent. Hence: reunion with God, fellowship resulting from this "tie that binds," and trust. That, in brief, is religion.

When a person truly has religion, as here described, his intellect is bound to be affected by it, not superficially, but thoroughly. And because his conscience is a function of the intellect, his conscience, too, will be affected in a thorough way.

True, all people have a conscience, even the head-hunting Dyaks in the interior of Borneo. Missionaries tell us that the Borneo savages have at least a modicum of knowledge of right and wrong. That is to say, they have ethics—of a sort. Conscience is universal because man has been created a rational being; is the image of a rational Divine Archetype.

But America's major religion, the Christian religion, teaches that when people have become "bound" to God, through the Spirit of Christ, and have true religion, the ordinary human conscience becomes attuned to the will of God as never before and a new morality buds forth and blossoms.

It is necessary to place this stress on conscience because our perplexities in sex life and procreation find their inception right there. And so a further and necessary question is: The voice of conscience, is it always, as some people believe, the voice of God?

The answer is no. People with some education have often come to that conclusion because the first syllable of the word "conscience" is considered to be the Latin for "with." And since the last part of the word has been derived from the Latin for "to know" they figured that "conscience," the complete word, means "to know along with (or together with) God." But the "con" in "conscience" does not mean "with." This particular "con" is an ancient Latin prefix which gives to the complete word the meaning of finality (to the final limits of one's knowledge). It also gives to the complete word the connotation of *judicial* knowledge (the conscience functioning as a judge). That is why the word "conscience" appears but seldom in classical Greek writings, but very plentifully in Roman writings, especially in those of Cicero. The Greeks were weak in judicial sense and temperament; the Romans strong.

So, conscience means the knowledge of one's inner self, just as a judge knows the man before the bar of justice after full investigation and the hearing of witnesses. And it also means judicial activity: the judge pronouncing his verdict according to the full extent of his knowledge.

But that leads to the question whether one's conscience cannot at times be mistaken. Upon that the answer is yes, and for either one of two reasons. One's conscience can be mistaken for lack of *sufficient* information, or for lack of *correct* information. In the latter case the information one has accumulated (as the result of home training, education, environ-

ment, etc.) may be ample, but it is in greater or lesser measure biased or warped, and therefore unsound.

And that takes us back to our book. The paramount aim
of our book is to help people—especially young married people—acquire an *informed and enlightened conscience* in matters of sex and reproduction. The structure of the book, its
prodigal offerings of the very latest in medical knowledge, its
forthrightness—all seek to achieve that specific end.

The writers will be found outspoken and frank. Some good
pious people feel that frankness in these matters is unseemly,
even unchristian. We don't go along with them. The human
procreative process has been Divinely conceived and ordered,
and we feel that in the past this highly important field has
been left too much and too long to spiritual illiterates and the
socially unwashed. As a consequence, much that is off color
and suggestive and downright smutty has beome associated
with it. We shall not be dissuaded by this unhappy condition.
We mean to tell the "facts of life," unabashed and without
mincing, having the welfare, happiness, and inner calm of the
morally mature public in mind.

It is our hope that very many people may be benefited by
the engrossing contents of this volume, that many problems
may be solved and annoying anxieties overcome, and that in
many ways a richer and more satisfying marital life may result.

JOHN CLOVER MONSMA

PART I

CONTROL OF CONCEPTION

BIRTH CONTROL

C. PAUL HODGKINSON

Dr. Hodgkinson, a Protestant, is Chairman of the Department of Gynecology and Obstetrics at Henry Ford Hospital, Detroit, Michigan.

The term "birth control" is really a euphemism; an expression by which people seek to disguise an act or practice about which they feel reticent and shy. Taking birth control literally it could mean pregnancy and all facets of obstetrical care. But it does not mean this. It means the prevention of conception to avoid pregnancy. Birth control is a cover-up term for *conception control.*

This innocent attempt at concealment serves to emphasize the "cloak-and-dagger" role the practice under discussion plays in modern thinking. Many people think of the practice as something stealthy, something that, if not downright illicit, had at least better be kept strictly private.

Such people, of course, are not adequately informed. Birth control (for convenience let us here use the popular term) represents a social problem of immense proportions. In its broadest sense it involves aspects of the social, the moral, the religious, the secular, the philosophic, the eugenic, and the demographic (pertaining to vital, or population, statistics). Some of that will become evident, I trust, in the present chapter.

Suppose we first take a brief look at the history of birth

control and related rules and customs, then consider what has been called the current population explosion, next comment upon the religious aspects of the subject, and finally become very practical and say something about the comparative value of a number of contraceptive means.

History

A review of the history of marriage shows that man has always been interested in the regulation of the birth of his progeny. From earliest times the legal bond of marriage between husband and wife has been believed necessary for the protection of children and society. Although the laws which govern marriage are highly variable, there is evidence that responsible man of all ages, cultures, and nations has felt it his obligation to regulate, at least to a certain extent, both the *qualitative* and the *quantitative* control of conception.

One of the earliest of regulations to govern *qualitative* control of the offspring was the law established for the marriage of blood relatives. The increased dangers of transmitting diseases of congenital, hereditary origin were recognized by some of the savage tribes. Hemophilia (the Disease of Kings, so named because it involved many of the male members of the royal families in Europe) serves as the best known example of the dangers of consanguinity. Both civil and church law prescribe how closely related a man and woman may be and still marry. Most states prohibit the marriage of first blood cousins. In England, rules of consanguinity, or blood relationship, are of church origin, and the Table of Consanguinity is printed in every prayer book.

In the United States there has in recent times been a tendency toward demanding additional legal marriage regulations for the protection of the health of the offspring. My home state of Michigan requires medical proof of the soundness of health. These precautions have as their primary objective the prevention of the transmission of venereal disease. Also, some states prohibit the marriage of persons confined to a public mental institution, on the basis that they are not sufficiently competent to give consent, unless and until proof of recovery is supplied by a certificate of health signed by two physicians.

Great strides have been made in the important field of genetics. Through the study of human chromosomes geneticists have shown that some diseases are transmitted as the result of defects in gene structure which may be hereditary. It is not farfetched to conceive that in the future the more practical couples will want to consult with a geneticist before finally deciding upon marriage.

There has also been a tendency over the years to exercise more control over *quantitative* conception. Probably the first law to govern the age of marriage was the Roman Law which established age fourteen for boys and twelve for girls. In some countries and in some states of the United States marriage between boys of fourteen and girls of twelve is still permitted. But there has been a tendency the world over to raise the marriageable age. In India, although weddings are still arranged by the parents, and engagements of the very young are still common, child marriages were prohibited by law in 1929. The marriageable age for the female in India has been raised from twelve to eighteen years. In the United States the tendency has been to raise the marriageable age to twenty-one years. The written consent of parents or guardians is required if the contracting parties are below the legal age.

Although Roman Law of fourteen years for boys and twelve for girls correlated the marriageable age with the average age for the initiation of physiologic reproductive function, man has recognized that marriage and childbearing carry more responsibility than simply the ability to procreate. By raising the marriageable legal age man gives evidence that he realizes maturity must be defined in terms other than reproductive capability. The age of twenty-one is a legal compromise—it is an average age when the average person attains emotional and social maturity; an age when a man and his wife can usually be counted upon to take their places in society as responsible citizens; an age when they can generally be depended upon to care adequately for their young and for themselves.

But raising the marriageable legal age has brought quantitative changes in the rate of conception. Although, thereby, the incidence of illegitimate pregnancy has become an alarming social factor that tends to offset to some extent any reduction in conception rate, the over-all effect is a considerable reduction in the number of babies born. During the life of the female, pregnancy is a physiologic possibility for an average period of thirty-three years, assuming that menstruation begins at age twelve and ends at age forty-five. And it is well known in medicine that occasionally conception can occur earlier than at age twelve. Considered from the standpoint of conception control, raising the marriageable age has been a legal effort to enforce sexual abstinence upon the maturing young, and this nine-year period of legally enforced sexual abstinence comes at a time of life when the physiologic sex drive is most compelling. Probably it is also the period in life of highest fecundity. Thus, in countries where civilization is considered to be most highly advanced, pregnancy and childbearing tend more and more to be controlled by legal fiat. Usually these countries are dominantly influenced by the Christian religion. The calculated resultant reduction in the physiologic potential of childbearing amounts to about 25 per cent.

In summary, while Christ came to elevate man in all respects, in the 1,963 years since the birth of Christ, history records that man has shown more interest in improving his domestic animals than he has in the selective breeding of his own kind. As for himself, he is willing to trust to luck, and many times he seems boldly to tempt and challenge nature to produce less than a perfect specimen. Through conception control as imposed by marriage laws he has shown increasing tendencies to limit somewhat the number of his offspring and slightly to improve their quality. Nevertheless, both with respect to quality and quantity of offspring man has through the ages made a poor showing, and only in the most recent modern times have certain faint indications of improvement and progress begun to multiply.

Population Explosion

Demography is the science of vital (or population) statistics. In plain words, it is the scientific study of births, deaths, and marriages. Demographers, the people who apply themselves to this study, usually are a quiet group of scientists, but recently they have thrust themselves upon a complacent world with the announcement of a threatening "population explosion." They tell us that the phenomenal increase in the birth rate and the more phenomenal decrease in the death rate have resulted in a population expansion of really menacing proportions. Should the present trend continue, so they say, then within a relatively few years people will be existing almost shoulder to shoulder, with insufficient space to provide food and shelter.

In these days of crop control and government farm subsidy, when farmers are being paid for not putting their land to productive use, the idea of crowding in the United States seems farfetched. Yet, let us look at the record in terms of the demographer.

The population density for the geographic area of any country shows the average number of people—men, women, and children—per square mile of land within its boundaries. Including our two new states, Alaska and Hawaii, the total land area of the United States now is 3,615,206 square miles. In 1790, with only 888,811 square miles of land, there were between four and five persons to each square mile. Except for Alaska and Hawaii, the total land area of the United States in 1860 was about the same as it is today. Then, the population density was 10.6 persons per square mile; by 1900 it was 25.6 persons per square mile; by 1950 it was 50.7. Admission of Alaska in 1959 brought in a very large land mass inhabited by very few people—571,000 square miles and 226,000 people. The admission of Hawaii in 1959, because of its relatively small size, made no difference in the nation's density of population. The 1960 census showed that the population density of the United States, including Alaska and Hawaii, was 50.5 persons per square mile of land—a five-times increase in the last 100 years.

Of the possessions of the United States, Puerto Rico has the largest population density: 643 persons per square mile, which is, incidentally, the highest in the world. Contrast this with the population densities of India and Japan, 245 and 469 respectively.

Rough estimates by world-population experts indicate that there are nearly three billion people in the world. The world population is increasing at the rate of about fifty million a year. About half of the world's people live in four countries: China, 690 million; India, 433 million; Soviet Union, 214 million; the United States, 185.4 million (February, 1962).

According to "United States Census of Population, 1960—Our Growing Population" (U. S. Government Printing Office) projections for the future indicate that our population will reach 215 million in 1970 and 261 million in 1980. Basically, how quickly or how slowly a population grows depends upon the number of births subtracted by the number of deaths that occur during any given period of time. This projection picture is based upon a surplus of fifteen, or twenty-four births less nine deaths per 1,000 population. During the 1950s, according to the publication just mentioned, the main factors in this trend were 41 million births and only 16 million deaths. In 1950 the birth rate for every 1,000 people in the United States was 24.1; in 1960 it was 23.4. Death rates for the same years were 9.6 and 9.3 respectively. All of which means that the population will double in forty years!

Although "birth control" is usually the first thought that comes to mind when we hear the term "population explosion," demographers show us that the more important factor is "death control." In the United States, as in most other countries with an educated population, the death rate continues to fall. In 1961 the number of people in this country over sixty-five years of age rose to 17.2 million, comprising 9.3 per cent of the total population. In the less-advanced countries social improvement through better education brings the benefits of modern medicine, public health, sanitation, and pestilence control. Food output is usually increased and death from famine is prevented. The striking improvement in longevity in Egypt is an example of how "death control" influences the population statistics. According to Guttmacher[1] in his excellent book, *Babies by Choice or by Chance,* from 1939 to 1952, Egypt's birth rate rose only from 46.4 to 49.9 per 1,000, but her death rate fell from 29.5 to 20.5.

Earlier it was mentioned that the term "birth control" was a euphemism that stood for "conception control." We have now found that the term "population explosion," as ordinarily understood, is also more or less of a misnomer. It has reference not only to lack of sufficient "birth control"; it also involves, and particularly, what might be called "progressive death control."

Religious Aspects

Any hope the physician ever had to compromise the religious, ethical, moral, social, legal, and, now, political influences of conception control has long since been lost in a sense of frustration and defeat. Most of his bewilderment comes

[1] Among the books Dr. Guttmacher has written on the general subject of Birth Control are:
Pregnancy and Birth, The Viking Press Inc., New York, 1957; New American Library, 1962. *Babies by Choice or by Chance,* Doubleday & Co., Inc., New York, 1959; Avon books, New York, 1960. *The Complete Book of Birth Control,* Ballantine Books, Inc., New York, 1961. For further information about Dr. Guttmacher see his chapter in this volume. —Editor.

from the different interpretations made by different religious groups of the questions of the ethics and morality of contraception.

History shows that the physician has a right to be confused. The religious, the moral, and the civil attitudes toward the progress of medical science, particularly as they affect population control, are in a state of hopeless confusion.

No religion, Christian or non-Christian, Protestant, Catholic, or Jewish; no moral interpretation, philosophic or practical; no civil code, Western or Eastern, regardless of the educated state of a population; advocates unrestricted contraception. On the other hand, all people, even the Catholics under certain circumstances, may use contraception in some form if they desire. According to Guttmacher, although the Marxist doctrine is as anticontraceptive as the Catholic, general birth rates in checkable Marxist countries have fallen from forty-seven per 1,000 in 1913 to twenty-six in 1955. The China policy reversed itself in 1958 from one of active contraception to a program of total anticontraception. Whether this change in attitude is due to an all-out adoption of the Marxist doctrine or due to Chou En-lai's belief of a coming all-out atomic world war, which he hopes to win, cannot be said. Guttmacher stated: "I think the simplest explanation of the widespread religious and political concern over any curtailment of full reproduction capacity is in terms of more and more parishioners, or more and more soldiers and workers." (See reference above.)

It seems safe to say that neither the Jew nor the Christian has received directly a Divine order to desist from using contraceptives. Whatever attitude is adopted, regardless of the religion, is the result of human interpretation. The first relevant Bible passage appears in Genesis: "Be fruitful, and multiply." (Gen. 1:28; 9:1) According to Williams[2] this passage was originally pronounced as a blessing, but later it

[2] Glanville Williams, *The Sanctity of Life and the Criminal Law,* Alfred A. Knopf, Inc., New York, 1957.

was interpreted by the rabbis as a duty imposed upon the male partner. The orthodox Jew interpreted this order literally. The modern Jew has an altered, more liberal opinion.

The second passage, also from Genesis, relates to the sin of Onan and has to do with the ancient Jewish law of levirate which directed that a dead man's brother must marry the widow if there were no sons.[3] This law is explained in Deuteronomy 25:5–10. Onan spilled his seed upon the ground to avoid the duty of levirate. He practiced *"coitus interruptus."* The Jewish Orthodox and Roman Catholic religions claim that Onan's act was evidence that *coitus interruptus* is a sin. Both Jews and Christians have rejected the institution of levirate since the tenth century, A.D.

Williams states that, in his opinion, the specific objection to contraception by many Christians is that "it is a legacy of the ascetic ideal, persisting in the modern world after the ideal itself has deceased." He states that with many early Christians the attitude toward marriage was largely negative, or, at least, indifferent. Celibacy was considered a virtue because of its denial of the desires of the flesh. It was a sort of rigorous test of moral fiber, a self-inflicted punishment that attested to the fervor of one's faith. The antisexual interpretation of a Christian's duty, says Williams, was derived from a passage in I Corinthians 7:1–9, in which the Apostle Paul states that it would be best if a man did not touch a woman but remained celibate as he himself was.[4]

---

[3] Genesis 38:8–10. This Scripture reference has been interpreted variously. See pp. 25, 40, 189 of this book.

[4] This quotation from St. Paul has been interpreted variously. Many New Testament scholars think that the Apostle wrote this because of the abnormality of the times—the furious, bloody persecutions of the Christians by the Roman government. He advised exceptional, temporary measures. Other New Testament scholars have advanced the thought that at the time of St. Paul's writings the end of the world was expected shortly. One scholar has stated that the quotation can be paraphrased this way: "If you are married, stay married; if you are single, stay single; the end is coming shortly anyway, so concentrate on your own salvation and that of others."

This same author states that St. Augustine (A.D. 354–430), in his *On the Grace of Christ and on Original Sin,* declared all carnal lust to be sinful. Marriage was justified on the basis that the evil of sexual lust was turned to good through the procreation of children. The scales of good and bad were balanced upon intent. So long as husband and wife toiled at procreation no sin was involved. Augustine declared that embraces of husband and wife which did not have procreation as their objective were concessions to an overbearing sexual desire and were in the range of forgiveness. This was considered a venial sin. The use of "evil appliance" to prevent propagation was a mortal sin. And this same author further states that Thomas Aquinas (A.D. 1225–74) "expressed the opinion that every carnal act deliberately done in such a way that generation cannot follow is a vice against nature and a sin ranking next to homicide, since the generation of offspring is impeded."

Catholics no longer hold these same rigid views about marital activities. Pope Pius XI in an encyclical (1930) allowed abstinence and use of the "safe period" (*coitus reservatus*) as methods to limit procreation. Guttmacher in his *Babies by Choice or by Chance* credits the Reverend Francis J. Connell, professor of moral theology at the Catholic University of America, with the following: "Some people believe that the Catholic Church teaches that a married couple are obliged to have as many children as is physically possible, but this is not true. The Catholic Church recognizes that at times a husband and wife have good reasons for not having any more children, at least for the time being . . . the only lawful way in which they can avoid having offspring or can space births of their children is abstinence from the use of their conjugal privileges, either total or periodic." And so it is clear that except for abstinence and the use of the "safe period" the Catholic Church opposes all methods of contraception.

The beliefs and attitudes of the large majority of the Protestants are quite different. The Protestant holds that it is his religious right and obligation to interpret God's ancient laws in the light of later revelations; to interpret the Old Testament in the light of the New. He believes in God's great gift of the Holy Spirit through whom He leads man to ascertain the "mind of Christ." He believes that it is man's obligation to re-evaluate and keep current the standards of his moral conduct according to the knowledge made available to him by Divine grace. Any apparently liberal attitude of the Protestant toward the control of conception is based upon health and the concept of reasonable family planning in the milieu of current-day living. Sexual desire as such is recognized as a biologic urge in physiologic man, not as a curse. Rather than a curse, the urge is recognized as God-implanted and therefore sacred. Immorality as it applies to contraception rests in intent, not in the physical device or means used for its accomplishment. In this last the attitude of the modern Jew is similar to that of the Protestant Christian.

Since a very large section of the American people believe in a wholesome practice of contraception, and since many among them still find themselves in the dark so far as details of the practice are concerned, it would seem beneficial at this point to dwell on those details to some extent. We shall try to be direct and practical in our description.

Methods of Contraception

If pregnancy is to occur following sexual intercourse, the male sperm cells must travel from the vagina into the uterus, and from there into the Fallopian tubes. This is a distance of from four to six inches, and for the sperm to travel this far several hours are required. The sperm cells meet the female ovum, or egg, near the open end of the Fallopian tube which lies near the ovary. When the capsule of the ovum is penetrated by a single male sperm cell conception is accomplished and pregnancy begins. If one wishes to have sexual intercourse and at the same time wishes to prevent pregnancy several methods are possible.

There is the *Safe Period* or *Rhythm* method. Because only one egg is released by ovulation each month, and because the egg can live but from twelve to eighteen hours unless it is fertilized, pregnancy can be prevented if intercourse is avoided several days before and several days after the expected time of ovulation. It is estimated that after intercourse the male sperm cells can live no longer than seventy-two hours. Therefore, using the "safe period" or "rhythm" method means avoiding intercourse for four days before and for four days after the expected time of ovulation. Some leeway must be allowed because the time of ovulation is not always the same each month.

Unfortunately, the time of ovulation cannot be determined ahead of time. Regardless of when ovulation occurs, the next menstrual period will occur fourteen days later. If the menstrual cycle is precisely twenty-eight days, ovulation can be expected to occur with reasonable certainty on or about the fourteenth day, counting from the first day of the previous menstrual period. If the menstrual cycle averages thirty-two days in length, the time of ovulation will be expected on the eighteenth day of the menstrual cycle. If the cycle is twenty-four days in length, ovulation will occur on the tenth day and intercourse must be avoided from the sixth to the fourteenth day.

This method of contraception is uncertain because most women have some variation in their menstrual cycle, and the time of ovulation cannot be calculated accurately. Testing for the time of ovulation by "fertility testers" or by basal temperature graphs is of little value because when the test indicates that ovulation has occurred it is already too late to prevent pregnancy if intercourse has occurred within a seventy-two-hour period.

Then there is the *Arrest of Sperm Migration* method. Pregnancy can also be prevented if some means are used to prevent the sperm from traveling into the uterus. This can be accomplished in three ways:

1. By penile condoms. The sperm can be deposited into a rubber or skin condom worn over the penis. Condoms are usually made of thin rubber or a thin membrane made from sheep's intestine. The *skin* condoms must be soaked in water before use. Some think that they have the advantage of dulling sensation less than condoms made of rubber. Rubber condoms are of excellent quality and, if used properly, seldom break.

2. By either the vaginal diaphragm or the cervical cap. The vaginal diaphragm is a thin rubber cap attached to a round, rubber-covered spring. It is inserted into the vagina by the woman prior to intercourse to form a partition between the vagina and the mouth of the womb (uterus) or cervix. It must be sufficiently large to extend from behind the pubic bone in the upper front part of the vagina to a position well behind the mouth of the womb, which is located in the back of the vagina. Prior to its insertion the rim and the cup of the diaphragm should be coated with contraceptive jelly. Use of the jelly not only kills the sperm but effectively seals the vagina around the diaphragm. Because the size of the vagina varies, each woman must be fitted for her diaphragm by her physician. Following intercourse the diaphragm should be left in place for at least six hours to allow the contraceptive jelly to kill the sperm effectively. Some women prefer to use a vaginal douche when they remove the diaphragm. Use of the vaginal diaphragm is an effective means of "birth control" when properly, and always, used. If repeated intercourse is desired, sooner than six hours, an application of contraceptive jelly should be inserted into the vagina, using the plastic applicator which comes with the jelly. The vaginal diaphragm is probably the most acceptable form of mechanical contraception for both partners. The disadvantages lie in the bother involved.

The cervical cap is a mechanical device made of rubber, plastic, or metal which fits over the cervix, or mouth of the womb. It must be accurately fitted by a physician and the patient must be thoroughly acquainted with its proper application. It is filled with spermicidal jelly and pressed over the cervix by manual pressure. When properly in place its position is maintained by suction. It may be left undisturbed for several days. The disadvantage of its use is the bother and skill involved in obtaining a proper fit. When properly used it is highly effective and compares favorably with the vaginal diaphragm.

3. By spermicides. Sperm migration into the uterus can be prevented through the use of vaginal preparations that immediately kill the sperm. Various vaginal jellies, creams, tablets, and suppositories have been used quite effectively by many couples. Although they have the advantage of convenience, they have not proved to be as effective as the diaphragm, cervical cap, or the condom. Another type of mechanical barrier to sperm migration recently made available consists of a vaginal foam. When placed into the vagina the cervix is covered with a layer of foamlike spermicidal jelly which not only kills the sperm but acts as a barrier to their migration. The efficiency of this preparation is at this time unproven, but the reports of the initial tests appear to be highly favorable.

The latest and probably the most effective means of contraception is the use of pills which have the property of preventing ovulation. The pills are popularly known as "oral contraceptive pills." Medically they are known as synthetic gestagens, and they have the combined hormonal properties of progesterone, estrogen, and testosterone. Two drugs are available and are known by their trade names as Enovid, (Searle and Company) and Norlutin (Parke Davis and Company). Both are equally effective in preventing ovulation and, hence, pregnancy. Although many women have taken these pills over long periods of time with apparent safety, recently reports have cropped up in the medical literature attributing certain rather serious side effects to their use. Any recommendation as to their use must be withheld at this time until the medical profession is certain that they can be used safely for contraceptive purposes.

In case the pills prove safe, their use is simple. One pill is taken each day by mouth, starting on the fifth day after the onset of menstruation. The medication is continued until twenty pills have been taken, when the drug is discontinued. Usually within one week a menstrual period occurs. The pills are again started on the fifth day after the onset of the menstrual flow. Occasionally, in some women, no menstrual period occurs. This does not indicate that the woman is pregnant. It usually means that the hormone medication has interfered with the woman's natural hormones so that no menstrual period will appear that month. Should this occur, and no physical harm is caused, the pills should be started again on the eleventh day after they were stopped. Again twenty pills should be taken on consecutive days. If no menstrual period occurs after they are stopped for the second time, a physician should be consulted. Perhaps the dose of the medication needs to be changed and the patient should be examined to make certain that she is not pregnant.

Not recommended, because they are not effective and reliable, are the vaginal douche and withdrawal (*coitus interruptus*). Also not recommended, because they are dangerous, are devices made of metal, rubber, or plastic which are placed within the uterus. One of the metal devices, the gold wishbone pessary, has been used in the past and many reports in medical literature tell of some of the dangerous complications that evolve. In the past doctors have considered such devices dangerous because of the low-grade chronic inflammation and infection that comes from their use. When contraceptive means of real worth and, to this date, proven safety are at woman's disposal, why trifle with means and methods that are in any way hazardous? The human body, also in contraceptive procedures, requires the utmost in thoughtfulness and care.

2

A PHYSICIAN LOOKS AT CONTRACEPTIVES

James R. Weir

Dr. Weir is a Specialist in Obstetrics and Gynecology. He lives in Monroe, Wisconsin, and is of the **Protestant** faith.

The problem of birth control is of necessary concern to any person who is involved in the practice of obstetrics as well as to the individuals in his care who have to meet this as a personal problem, and also to all the members of the clergy who without exception regard this as a religious and moral problem.

Birth control has been the subject of ethical and religious controversy for many years, and the controversy has been intensified in recent times by the availability of an oral tablet or pill which is an effective contraceptive agent.

Let me say at the outset that in considering some of the issues involved I speak out of my own thinking and experience, independently of others. The Christian physician cannot divorce his beliefs from his medical practice, nor can he solve what he considers to be a moral problem by referring it to a physician who may seem to be less concerned, personally, about moral values. This makes it imperative that the physician be clear in his own mind as to his personal attitude toward birth control practices.

The nonprofessional reader would be surprised at the large number of requests that come to any physician with an active obstetrical practice for advice regarding birth control and for prescriptions for contraceptive devices. In my own case it happens daily. Because of strong and opposing opinions held by various groups the subject is often a source of severe mental conflict and anxiety to the patient. Fellow-physicians and myself are often called upon to resolve these conflicts, and one cannot help but observe the distressing effects that various views and practices in connection with birth control oftentimes have upon the marriage ties themselves.

Psychology enters here, too. Before advice is given by the physician he must be acquainted, not only with the religion of the individual patient, but also with the intensity of his or her belief in order not to precipitate severe guilt feelings that may have untoward effects on the patient's emotional stability.

In view of the position in which we as physicians are placed with regard to birth control practices, it is somewhat surprising that a review of current medical literature reveals very little of the medical views on birth control. Is the subject being considered more or less extraneous? Or is the matter considered settled? A recent editorial in the *Journal of the American Medical Association* seems to proceed on that assumption. It pointed out the need for effective contraceptives and indicated the author's impatience with those who oppose birth control for religious reasons.

In general it may be said that scientific medicine upholds the right of the physician to prescribe contraceptives. This became unusually clear in a recent court case in Connecticut where an attempt to defend the physician's right to prescribe contraceptives received support from physicians of the Protestant, Roman Catholic, and Jewish faiths as they enlisted to aid the physician-defendant. Some of these witnessing physicians held faculty positions in Catholic medical schools.

On the other hand, the physician who is looking to scientific medicine to crystallize his thinking along the lines of birth control and contraceptives receives no help, and the border between ethical and unethical practice seems very vague indeed. Generally it may be said that in this country medicine assumes that the physician has the right to prescribe contraceptives as long as the method employed does not interfere with the health of the patient.

After years of medical practice I am still amazed at the complex process of conception and at the fact that the human race maintains such a high degree of fertility, considering the multiplicity of factors involved. Take the process of conception. This has been studied intensively for many years, and although there are areas which are not completely understood the general chain of events involving many body systems has been outlined. What marvels of Divine creative wisdom and power! The pituitary gland at the base of the brain, whose function is in part controlled by the brain and the emotions, elaborates hormones which are carried by the blood stream and stimulate the cyclic function of the ovaries. These hormones cause the production and maturation of the ova (eggs). The ovum, the maternal contribution to the hereditary background of the fetus, passes through one of the two Fallopian tubes and enters the uterine cavity. The lining of the uterus is prepared by two types of hormones from the ovaries to receive the ovum. If fertilization takes place the sperm carrying the hereditary background of the father ascends by means of its own motility through the cervix or neck of the uterus, passes through the uterus, and enters the Fallopian tube where union with the ovum occurs and the cell divisions begin which ultimately become an infant carrying the hereditary background of both parents.

In order for pregnancy to occur a number of systems must function properly. The hormone balance between the ovary and the pituitary must be maintained. This balance may be destroyed by malfunction of the thyroid and adrenal glands. The ovary must contain normal ova and be able to release these upon the pituitary stimulation. The Fallopian tubes must be patent (open) and contain functioning cilia which help direct the ova into and down the tube. The uterine cavity must be able to respond to the ovarian hormones and possess a lining capable of promoting the attachment and development of the fetus. The cervix must produce secretions that are not harmful to the sperm. The sequence of events in the male are not less complicated, and of course the fetus must receive from both parents the proper genes to determine the normal development of the vital structures and organs necessary for its own existence.

In other words, when we talk about contraception and contraceptives we are dealing with an extremely complicated mechanism, one of the Creator's most exquisite and marvelous accomplishments, and He would expect us to act very circumspectly. The methods of contraception will not be discussed here. That has been done by a very capable colleague in the first chapter of this volume, and I refer the reader to it. What I wish to comment on is the philosophy back of contraceptive procedures. Is the use of contraceptives permitted? Is it *ever* permitted? Where is our authority for it? With whom rests the decision in particular cases?

Practically all Americans of mature age know that Catholics and Protestants have different views on contraception, a difference that springs primarily (though not exclusively) from their different theologies. The Catholic Church regards marriage as a sacrament, and the Church has built its theories on that doctrine ever since the time of Augustine (*circa* A.D. 400). Protestants deny that marriage is a sacrament; believe that it belongs to the Divine institutions of natural life.

The Catholic Church also contends that birth prevention is contrary to natural law. This writer cannot go along with that. The antinatural-law theory has a fundamental wrongness antecedent to any ecclesiastical law or tradition. The concept of natural law can hardly be called a "Christian" concept. It originated with the pagan Stoics who so classified those laws which could be determined by reason to belong to the fixed regularities of nature. But many of those regularities are being temporarily lifted or suspended by the inventions of modern science, much to the benefit of humanity.

As a physician I have been dealing with both Catholics and Protestants, and I have my problems. Contraceptive practices not permitted by the Catholic Church are considered sinful, and the confession of such practices is required in the confessional. The intent is often all-important, and interpretation of the intent of a person allows a certain leeway of liberality in the seemingly uncompromising stand of the Church.

When the contraceptive tablet or pill came on the market and became widely used, also by Catholics, the problem of intent became a very soul-searching one for the conscientious and devout Catholics. For Enovid, or Norlutin, is not only a contraceptive but is also used for the regulation of the menstrual cycles. Are Catholic women really using this pill to control their irregular menstrual periods or are they basically trying to prevent a pregnancy? That is a critical point for the confessional. The doctor, being aware of this problem, will usually attempt to prevent guilt feelings by emphasizing the need for control of the menstrual cycle and by only incidentally mentioning the effect as a contraceptive, although he knows this may be a not undesirable side effect. This same approach has been used for years in the essentially similar decision of hysterectomy (a sterilizing procedure) for *benign* uterine fibroids. This procedure is more apt to be done in Catholic patients when sterility is a desirable side effect. It differs, however, from the foregoing in that the onus of the decision is placed once and for all in the hands of the physician instead of being a daily decision, largely made by the patient as she swallows the pill in the morning.

The Catholic Church does condone the use of the rhythm method of birth control, but this method is hardly dependable. In fact, it has many drawbacks, a discussion of which does not lie within the framework of this particular chapter.

In contrast to the open and widely understood stand of the Catholic Church, the Protestant position seems confused and for the most part not well understood by both the clergy and the general church membership. I cannot remember ever having heard the subject of birth control mentioned from the pulpit; and since the average Protestant minister, even though he be well versed in the matter, does not have the chance for intimate contact with the members of his congregation which the Catholic confessional affords, there are large numbers of Protestants who remain entirely ignorant of the position of their Church or denomination on the subject of birth control. It is true that the Protestants have frequently expressed themselves on the subject of birth control. The World Council of Churches, the National Council of Churches, the International Missionary Council, and other interchurch bodies have made their thoughts known. Among the Protestant denominational bodies the United Presbyterian Church has perhaps gone the farthest when its General Assembly, in May, 1962, decided to "urge our (Federal) Government to assist other countries . . . which seek our help in this matter, to develop programs of responsible family planning and conception control in meeting problems of rapid population growth." In addition the General Assembly of this Church "urged the United Nations and its agencies to assist countries seeking help in this matter to develop programs of responsible family planning and conception control . . ." But these official decisions have, generally speaking, not reached the masses—the general church membership. There is a real need to inform the average Protestant married couple regarding their Church's views on the subject of birth control. This is a subject for pastoral premarital counseling, and might also be an appropriate subject for discussion among young married groups in the church. The subject can be brought up in discussions of the Scriptural references to marriage and the married life.

No direct statements regarding birth control are found in the Bible, but marriage is declared a Divine institution designed to form a permanent union between a man and a woman, and within the bounds of this institution and this union sexual intercourse is freely permitted. The Apostle Paul states with all clarity that sexual intercourse between married people is a pure and sinless act, and he prescribes no limits of any kind (Heb. 13:4 and other places). Children are still "a heritage of the Lord," but they do not constitute the sole purpose of marriage, according to Scripture. With all this in mind, does it not follow that the Christian physician should take the same pains in helping to preserve a marriage that he takes in the preservation of life itself?

The physical union between man and wife strengthens the spiritual union, and the completeness and satisfactory fulfillment of each type of union depends upon the other. The spiritual is completed by the physical and the physical relationship of marriage is seriously disturbed when spiritual unity does not exist. In fact, sexual adjustment and compatibility are not achieved by some technique, or an intimate knowledge of male and female anatomy, or a deep understanding of reproductive physiology, but by a climate engendered by daily acts of love for each other and true mutual devotion. In most cases of maladjustment which develop after marriage the cause is not to be found in some deep-seated sexual or psychological problem of either partner but in the depth, extent, and expression of their spiritual union. Do they love and respect each other, and do they show it undeniably toward each other in their daily tasks? Or are they, either one of them or both, selfish and self-centered? It makes a difference—intrinsically!

Let me speak out freely. This is still our free America —for everybody, regardless of what our religion may be. So let there be complete freedom of friendly discussion, also in this important social matter of marriage and the permissiveness or nonpermissiveness of contraception.

In my opinion, Protestants, taking them by and large, have failed to emphasize the significance of marriage; Catholic leaders, through extra-Biblical teachings, have misinterpreted the sacred bond. This unfortunate situation, in both church groups, is the source of much confusion and actual mental agony of many married couples today in the matter of birth control. Many families are forced by reasons of health, mental or physical, or by the economic realities of a nonagricultural society, to limit family size. The Catholic Church recommends that this limitation be achieved by continence; that marriage cease to be a physical union—only a spiritual one. Sleeping in separate beds is advised. Why not separate rooms or, still more effective, separate houses? I exaggerate, but the effect on the spiritual union of the marriage is great, whichever the arrangements.

It is my conviction that the use of contraceptives is permitted—any time that both husband and wife agree to resort to such use. And my authority in this matter is the Bible, our sacred Constitution for spiritual and ethical living. Nowhere does the Bible assail the principle of contraception. Nowhere does it prohibit its use. The case of Onan, often cited, does not apply here.[1] It only indicates that at least one certain form of contraception was known in those ancient times. Onan was punished for violating a fixed social rule of patriarchal times.

A Christian's belief regarding the use of contraceptives must be related to the meaning and purpose of marriage as determined by a study of Scripture. Scripture does not consider marriage, first and above all, as a vehicle for rearing a family. It ascribes to marriage the deeper meaning of the spiritual and physical union of man and wife illustrating and symbolizing the relation between the "Bridegroom" and the "Bride"—Christ and the true Church (Rev. 21:9 and other places).

Attempts to avoid pregnancy by restricting the physical union (that is, by abstaining from sexual intercourse) may be disastrous to a marriage, and it certainly would deprive marriage of the fullness of its true character. Yet it may be

[1] Genesis 38:8–10. This Scripture reference has been interpreted variously. See pp. 11, 40, 189 of this book.

necessary in today's conditions of urban living and rapidly expanding populations to restrict the size of one's family. And so contraception becomes a logical requisite—high grade, untainted, and God-approved.

3

BIRTH CONTROL—PERMISSIVE AND NECESSARY

William C. Johns

> **Dr. Johns** is a Specialist in Obstetrics and Gyne-
> cology at Encino Medical Plaza in Albuquerque,
> New Mexico. He is a member of the **Presbyte-
> rian Church.**

The subject of birth control has many facets.
Primarily, there are the religious, the ethical, and the medical
implications of the subject.

Let us first consider whether there are logical Biblical reasons validating the use of birth control, or whether there is
Biblical teaching against it. To obtain an adequate answer it
must be decided whether, according to Scripture, procreation
is the only or, at least, the basic function of sex in marriage.
With those questions answered we shall consider the dissemination of contraceptive knowledge to other, less-privileged
parts of the world, not only from a political and governmental, but also, and especially, from a Christian-agency
standpoint. We feel that special stress on this latter point is
called for and shall make it the leading thought of the present
chapter.

As a matter of terminology we might say that "conception
control" is a better term than "birth control." It describes
more exactly what is meant—the effective prevention of pregnancy. "Birth control" covers the entire birth process, from
conception to confinement. The larger aspect of conception

control as it applies to countries rather than to individuals is more logically expressed by the term "fertility regulation" rather than the more common term of "population control."[1]

The Scriptures point to at least two basic functions of sex in marriage: first, the nourishment of love and companionship; secondly, procreation. Christ's teachings about the purposes of marriage deal primarily with the love and companionship aspect. The Apostle Paul deals in a more detailed way with sex. He writes: "The wife hath not power over her own body, but the husband; and likewise also the husband hath not power over his own body, but the wife. Defraud ye not one the other except it be with [mutual] consent for a time, that ye may give yourselves to fasting and prayer; and come together again, that Satan tempt you not for your incontinency." (I Cor. 7:4, 5) In another New Testament epistle we read, "Marriage is honorable in all, and the bed undefiled." (Heb. 13:4) In the former passage it is pointed out that it is unwise and dangerous for couples to have long periods of abstinence, for most couples need regular coitus (sexual intercourse) for the nourishment of love and companionship, both of a spiritual and a physical kind.

The act of sexual intercourse is referred to in the Bible on numerous occasions, be it usually in poetic and oriental language, with the stress on love and companionship. Also, several times the joy of having children and responsibilities toward them are discussed. There is no implication in Scripture that one of these ends is primary or more important than the other. Protestant bodies have generally held that they are both primary functions of marital sexual activity—the nourishment of love and companionship, and procreation. They have been considered coequal. The Roman Catholic teaching on the other hand is that mutual love and companionship and all that is needed for them are subordinate to parenthood.

[1] See Richard M. Fagley, *The Population Explosion and Christian Responsibility,* Oxford University Press, New York, 1960.

In considering the Christian meaning of marriage it should be realized that marriage is much more than a simple agreement between husband and wife. It is a covenant between the two and God; a significant Divine act. This union somehow makes the two a single personality. Richard Fagley suggests a third end in marriage—a "Divine vocation."[2] The Apostle Paul, as we know, has compared the union of Christ and His Church with the marriage relationship (Eph. 5:23–33).

A few years ago a group of scholarly theologians met in Oxford University, England, to study the population problem and in that connection marriage and its meaning. They issued what became known as the Mansfield Report, and this report states, "Marriage as a Divine institution can be described in Biblical terms as a convenanted relationship within which man and woman receive the grace, security, and joy promised by God to those who are faithful to it. Marriage is the great mystery which still illuminates for men the covenant or marriage of Jehovah with Israel (Hos. 2:19) and of Christ with His Bride, the Church (Eph. 5:23–33; Rev. 21:9; 22:17). Thus the covenanted relationship of husband and wife within marriage is, in the purpose of God, one of total commitment, a total giving of self and a total acceptance of the other, resulting in a union, spiritual and physical, described in the Bible as becoming 'one flesh.' "[3]

It should be evident at this point that procreation is not the only, and not necessarily the primary, function of sex in marriage. "They twain [two] shall be one flesh," asserted He through whom all things were made, and we of the modern day may be glad that, thanks to medical progress and under Divine blessing, that sacred dictum can be carried out with

[2] For those interested in Fagley's idea, see *Population Control—The Imminent World Crisis,* by Melvin G. Shimm, Oceana, Duke University Press, 1961.

[3] *Ecumenical Study Group on Responsible Parenthood and the Population Problem,* Mansfield College, Oxford, England, 1959.

greater contentment and less trepidation than ever before. We can now proceed to a brief consideration of how we, Christian "Westerners," can use our contraceptive knowledge for the benefit of foreign lands and peoples that go bent under the terrific weight of overpopulation.

The historical background of population growth is interesting and very applicable to a discussion such as this. At the time of Christ there were approximately 250 million people on the earth. The rate of growth during the next 1,650 years was very slow. In fact, it seemed to rise and fall in cycles, with a gradual increase, until it reached about 500 million.[4] This gradual growth reflected the high death rate, due to frequent famines, frequent epidemics of diseases, and to wars. For the world to maintain its population and have a fair amount of growth the productivity of the woman needed to be used to a high, if not the highest, degree. With the discovery of other lands in the seventeenth century, the increase in technological understanding, and the decreasing frequency of widespread epidemics (though disease was far from controlled), the rate of population growth began to rise much more rapidly, and by 1950 the world population was estimated to be just under three billion, having tripled in the last hundred years during a time of medical and scientific advancement. The rate of population growth now the world over is 1.7 per cent per year, and this rate is steadily increasing.[5]

Now, the following is important: The rate of population growth has increased much more rapidly than the average in those underdeveloped countries where there has been a rapid *decrease* in the death rate because of foreign aid from the

[4] Robert C. Cook, in *Population Control—The Imminent World Crisis,* by Melvin G. Shimm, Duke University Press, 1961.

[5] Alan F. Guttmacher, *Clinical Experience with Practical Techniques for the Use of Enovid in Ovulation Control.* Transcript of a Closed Circuit Television Symposium, G. D. Searle & Co., Chicago, 1961.

"have" nations. At the present rate of growth the world population will double in less than forty years and will be quadrupled in seventy-five years.

But there is more. Both as a Christian nation and for reasons of national security and commercial expansion we have been led to give economic and educational aid to many underdeveloped countries. This has had the effect of greatly increasing their internal requirements for food, shelter, schools, old-age care, etc. But it has also greatly increased their birth rate, and the rate at which newborn babies remain alive.

What I mean to say is that if we fail to provide a far more *radical* solution of their problems, that is, a way to decrease their birth rate, we are giving them solutions that are altogether imperfect, and we actually compound their many problems. Here are the many, many countries of Asia, Africa, the islands of the sea, our own hemisphere, with their hundreds of millions of inhabitants. What can we do for them? How can we get to the bottom of their troubles? Let us try to visualize that well-nigh limitless sea of downtrodden, ignorant, emaciated, sickly, and hungry human beings, listless because of centuries of stupefying woe. What, if anything, can we do for them that will *really* help?

We can teach them birth control! As a Protestant may I say that in the educational divisions of our evangelistic and missionary programs significant action must be taken for the dissemination of fertility-control knowledge. Let denominational boards get busy! Let our pastors and missionaries in the field establish contact with intelligent and receptive native headmen and tribal chieftains! Let instruction classes be started! The news is bound to spread.

Readers who have some knowledge of contraceptives will perhaps say to themselves, or amongst themselves, that if the majority of the women in foreign-mission fields are as unintelligent and ignorant as they are reported to be, then such women could never cope with the mechanical and chemical means used for the control of conception. And we grant they may be partly right. The diaphragm-and-jelly, the cervical cap, vaginal suppositories, vaginal tablets, spermatocidal jellies or creams, contraceptive foam—all these and others might prove too much for blurred minds and hard-driven people.

But there are also vast numbers of "natives" that would surprise you with their general alertness. And there are many others who are innately bright; only they have never had a chance to "bring it out."

So far as the general masses are concerned, however, the most wonderful thing that happened for them happened only two years ago when our Food and Drug Administration approved physiologic contraception means—*physiologic* in distinction from mechanical and chemical means. Very extended research and experimentation preceded this approval, particularly in Puerto Rico and Haiti, and there is still no *perfect* contraception. But the drug approved by the FDA (known to the American public as Enovid or Norlutin, depending upon the pharmaceutical source) is certainly pretty close to perfection. It represents a new technique of birth control which operates by altering the physiology of the female body so as to render conception temporarily impossible. (Further medical details of this new contraceptive are given in the first chapter of this volume, and there is no need to duplicate.)

The beauty of this physiologic contraceptive for women in underdeveloped lands is its simplicity—the very simple way of using it: just swallowing a pill in the morning for the larger part of each month. This method can be very easily taught to even the simplest minds, and the thing for us Americans to do is to ask our missionaries and missionary helpers to get busy all over the globe and to start shipping the medications out in volume.

Although this matter of fertility control has so far been mentioned in terms of world-wide problems and moral obligations of our country and people toward less-favored parts of the world, yet it was not implied that anybody but the individual couple should make the final decision as to their personal use of any contraceptive method. In our own United States, the land of hard-won freedom, there should be no state or federal laws whatsoever to limit an individual couple's right to decide for themselves whether and when family limitation is wise and desirable. Nor should any other agency, of whatever nature, attempt to dictate matters that by Divine ordinance belong to the private, inner counsels of man and wife.

The social-medical defense in favor of the use of fertility control is unequivocal. The health of the mother, though this is an individualized consideration, is certainly not improved by rapidly recurring pregnancies over her full years of fertility. Many women who are emotionally able to care for two or three children are not equipped to supervise six or eight. On the other hand, the mortality rate of childbearing women has changed for the better. With modern medical advances women who three decades ago had an extremely high mortality rate because of heart disease, diabetes, or hypertension, now in the large majority of cases can safely become pregnant. In serious cases, however, there is too much risk and pregnancy should be avoided.

The other aspect of the social-medical defense of family planning is the consideration of the physical, emotional, and economic well-being of the offspring. No over-all rule can be laid down because circumstances vary with family groups. The physical, emotional, and financial capabilities of families, as well as the resources of the surrounding communities— they all vary. Usually the best interest of a family is not met if rapidly repeated pregnancies are allowed to occur.

We can state with great satisfaction that genuine advances have been made in simplification and effectiveness of conception control, and we hope that further research may bring still greater blessings.

4

NATURAL LAW AND
BIRTH CONTROL

William J. Egan

> **Dr. Egan** is prominent in **Roman Catholic** medi-
> cal circles. He is a Specialist in Obstetrics and
> Gynecology, and makes his home in Brookline,
> Massachusetts.

Birth control deprived me of a tutor at Har-
vard. When I started my medical education a tutor was as-
signed to be my director, adviser, and big brother for the
four years. According to custom, for our first meeting I was
invited to his home for dinner. Conversation began with his
suggestion that he, as a Catholic, was appointed as my tutor
so that he could undo in the next four years all the antiquated
notions of child spacing which I had been spoon fed in my
scholastic philosophy classes at college. Conversation ended
at three o'clock in the morning when I asked, "How do you
make a good confession?" He replied that he did not mention these points to his confessor, for "it was none of the confessor's business." When I suggested that this was improper
thinking, we adjourned—with never a second session. His
parting salute was that each man was entitled to the convictions for which he had a sound basis.

I propose to explain the basis of my own convictions. In
this explanation my steps will be the following: (1) proof of
the existence of the Creator; (2) the existence of His laws
(natural law); (3) the existence of a soul subject to those

laws; (4) the child-spacing methods consistent with procreation and the Creator's laws.

Thus, I hope that tolerance and clearer understanding of the way of life in Catholic marriage may ensue.

Now, were I to present to you a watch, you would be convinced from its intricate mechanism, accuracy, and purpose that it must have had an intelligent designer. The designer intended that his watch should be used to tell time. That was his purpose in making it. It was not to be used as a hammer, a spoon, or a radio. To suggest that it could be used as such, even by accident, would be wrong to the point of being ridiculous. In addition, for this watch to tell time accurately certain rules must be obeyed, e.g., it must be wound regularly, it must be protected from exposure, it must be cleaned at intervals, it must be removed from magnetic fields. Following such rules, the designed instrument would serve its purpose and tell time throughout its mechanical life. I should stress that intelligence and reason tell us that this watch could not possibly happen and exist by accident.

Likewise, when I offer for your consideration your own baby, through boyhood and adolescence to manhood, reason again tells you that that baby is no accident. Besides, no matter how intricate the watch may be, this human mechanism is so vastly more complex that research has explained only a fraction of its functioning parts. Indeed, the greatest scientist has not been able to reproduce in vitality one of its simplest parts: the fingernail. When you consider further the ability of this little body to process foods into cell nutrition; the interrelationships of vital glands (pituitary, thyroid, adrenal); the transmission of impulses from the brain to the muscles, for muscle activity; then surely you must admit a supremely intelligent Creator. Call Him what you will; most of us call Him God.

As with the watchmaker and the watch, certain rules are obvious between God and the creature. These apply to all men, *from* all time and *to* all time, and they are changeless. They are the Designer's plans by which the creature functions normally. For each segment of creation—stars, planets, animals, trees, plants—additional plans or rules are deductible. Altogether, these are called the laws of nature. And these laws of nature have existed since creation; they apply to all creatures regardless of the belief or disbelief of individual rational creatures; and they are operative everywhere.

No man denies that he is superior to the animals. In the recognition of this superiority man tacitly admits his capacity to think, to analyze, to distinguish, to hate, to love, to remember—all attributes of the spirit, of something that is beyond the material, and of something that no surgeon operating or pathologist at post-mortem has been able to demonstrate. Yet it is something that is obviously present in the man alive and absent in the man dead.

This spirit, which Christians call the soul, is again a product of the Creator. Knowledge of the nature of the soul cannot be established by reason alone. In his encyclical *Humani generis* Pope Pius XII confirmed this with these words: "For the truths that have to do with God and the relations between God and men transcend completely the sensible order. . . . In the acquisition of such truths the human intellect is hampered not only by the impulses of the senses and the imagination but also by the evil passions stemming from original sin. As a result, men readily persuade themselves in such matters that what they do not wish to be true is false or at least doubtful." Knowledge of the spirit of man is readily available, however, from three sources: (1) the Bible—the Scriptures of the Old and New Testaments; (2) tradition—accepted and orthodox theology held and preached by the Fathers of the Church and left by them as a precious heritage; (3) revelation—God showing from time to time by appearance and by miracle His intent, demands, and direction.

Herein lies the point of departure between the Catholic view of family planning and that of many other segments of the population. If you deny the Creator, the human spirit, and the fact of creation and all that is connected with it, then you accept, logically, sexual license—though many times the acceptance of the latter is what leads to denial of the former. Nor can it be alleged that all Catholics (like my tutor, for instance) accept carte blanche the Catholic opinion. Acceptance among Catholics varies with depth of faith, degree of intelligence, amount of knowledge of God and creation, type of education, ratio of unselfishness, and heights of spiritual striving. Of each man's attainments in these spheres he himself is the poorest judge. As a poor judge, he is without the right to rate the merits of his fellow man. Again, to allege that Catholic opinion is not valid because many Catholics do not conform to it is the same as saying that in our national life we have no federal laws because so many citizens flout them. The laws are there, and conformity or lack of it does not change them.

As a physician, I mull over these facts; realize that I am no expert in matters spiritual; seek a consultation. From the experts, the moral theologians and their writings, emerges the following factual information:

From the Creator's design of man and of woman as separate but complementary mates it is apparent that He intended the sex act for procreation. Making a purely physical appraisal, it is obvious that the sex act can be accomplished without resultant pregnancy. This is due to the fact that ovulation occurs in females usually only once a month. If He had intended that pregnancy result from each sex act, He would have seen to it that a receptive ovum, or egg, was constantly available. Since He did not, He granted the possibility of sexual pleasure as an additional attribute of mating.

In the positive act of procreation six steps are necessary: (1) preparation for the act; (2) penetration; (3) insemination—the deposition of the seed; (4) fertilization; (5) pregnancy; (6) labor and delivery. The first three steps comprise the voluntary contribution of the married partners. After the third step, nature takes over. If an egg is present, steps four to six follow naturally. If no egg is present, nature, still operating normally, voids steps four to six. But the six steps are *one natural continuity*. The first need not be taken. Once it is taken, any interference with or omission of the subsequent steps is a violation of the natural continuity, vitiates nature, and hence is wrong. (At this point it would be well to point out that artificial insemination is not in harmony with this continuous act of procreation. Since steps one and two are omitted and only step three is present, the natural course is vitiated and for it is substituted an experiment in animal husbandry.)

In this succession (of procreation) there is no obligation that the married partners have two, five, ten, or twenty children. Nor have I found a moral theologian who alleges that there is. The only demand is that, as in the use of a watch, if the act is to be used it must be used correctly and in accordance with natural, Divinely established laws. The end, even though it be good, does not justify abnormal means. So, no hygienic, eugenic, social, or economic need can be used as an argument to thwart the laws of the Creator.

What form of family planning can be used, then, to meet health, social, or economic demands? In short, how can the married couple live up to their marital obligations of the natural law and at the same time adjust themselves to the material restrictions of their state in life? Three methods are known at present:

1. *Nursing*. It is a scientific fact that the only purpose of the female breast is to nurse babies. While the mother is producing milk and nursing, the ovaries are in a resting state and do not ovulate. Gynecologists agree that this is true in about 90 per cent of the women. Hence, nursing of offspring is an effective and natural method of child spacing.

2. *The Safe Period*. Earlier in the discussion mention was made of the fact that the female ovulates once a month, usu-

ally. This cyclic rhythm can be disarranged by disorders of metabolism, psychic shocks, and emotional tensions. In a majority of the women, however, a definite time of ovulation can be predicted by the calendar. More recently, this time can be pinpointed with greater accuracy by basal temperatures (the variations in body temperature when at rest). Still newer research has shown that an additional test of ovulation is the change in the sugar content of the vaginal secretions. Sexual intercourse by married partners in a naturally "safe period" does not contravene nature.

3. *Total Abstinence.* Provided that both partners agree to abstain, no action is taken that breaks the rules of the Maker. Unless both agree, one may complain justifiably that he is being deprived of his marital right. This abstinence is legitimate family planning on the one hand and a reaffirmation on the other that the married partners are helpmates to each other in saving their souls. Again, self-discipline is the mark of a responsible man in contrast to the irresponsible animal. This is the only alternative when, due to irregularity of ovulation and periods, use of the "safe period" in family planning is not possible.

In sum: God's laws of procreation are deductible from reason and revelation. Any act performed in accordance with them is right; all other acts in the sex life are wrong. The sanction imposed by God is graphically noted by St. Augustine: "Intercourse even with one's legitimate wife is unlawful and wicked where the conception of the offspring is prevented."

5

CONTRACEPTION PAST
AND PRESENT

ALAN F. GUTTMACHER

> **Dr. Guttmacher** is Obstetrician and Gynecologist-in-Chief at the Mount Sinai Hospital in New York City. He is President of the Planned Parenthood Federation of America, Inc., and belongs to the **Reformed Jewish** faith.

In my opinion the strict taboo by the early Hebrews of contraception and the induction of abortion stems from the demographic, or population, problem which faced them. They were a small, nomadic group with the mission to transmit to the rest of the world their philosophical ideal of "one God." Surrounded by hostile neighbors, their sheer survival to permit them to preach monotheism depended upon an increase in their numbers—more soldiers, workers, and breeders. Therefore, the Old Testament exhorts the Jew "to be fruitful and multiply."

It seems apparent that some Jews were evading the responsibility to multiply by employing contraception, and the method used was withdrawal by the male: *coitus interruptus*. In order to outlaw that only popular contraceptive technique of Bible times the story of Onan is told in Genesis, chapter 38. This by implication interdicts not only *coitus interruptus*, but all birth control.[1]

[1] Genesis 38:8–10. This Scripture reference has been interpreted variously. See pp. 11, 25, 189 of this book.

It is my heretical opinion that if the Bible were written today, with our three billion global population (to become over six billion in the year 2000), instead of exhorting us to "be fruitful and multiply," it would say, "be ye careful," or some similar phrase.

According to Josephus, the Jews were also very rigid in regard to the induction of abortion. They meted out punishment not only to the abortionist but also to the woman upon whom the abortion was performed. They endowed the fetus with certain rights and a state of inviolability.

The early Christians had the identical population problem —lack of adherents, persecution, and martyrdom—which faced the early Hebrews. For that reason St. Augustine took over *in toto* the Hebraic attitude toward contraception and the *conceptus*. This attitude came down unmodified through the intervening centuries—until very recently.

Before we discuss modifications in the viewpoints of Judaism and Christianity, I should like to explore the attitude of the Roman contemporaries of the early Christians. The authority I shall quote is Soranus, the greatest gynecologist and one of the greatest physicians of antiquity. He was born a Greek on the island of Ephesus and after receiving a medical education migrated to Rome, where he became the most important physician in that great world capital during the reigns of emperors Hadrian and Trajan. He wrote his famous *Gynecology* about A.D. 130. This book was lost for more than one thousand years, until in 1830 a manuscript copy was found by the German physician-scholar Friedrich Dietz as he browsed through Paris' *Bibliothèque Nationale*. Soranus was so great a physician that he received the accolade of being appointed physician to the gladiators—odd employment for a gynecologist. However, he was a prominent physician in a variety of fields and wrote books on surgery of the eye, fractures, therapeutics, and pathology.

Chapter twenty-nine of Soranus' *Gynecology* is titled, "Whether One Ought to Make Use of Abortives and Contraceptives, and How." We quote in part:

"A contraceptive differs from an abortive, for the first does not let conception take place, while the latter destroys what has been conceived.

"But a controversy has arisen. One party banishes abortives, citing the testimony of Hippocrates who says, 'I will give to no one an abortive'; moreover, because it is the specific task of medicine to guard and preserve what has been engendered by nature. The other party prescribes abortives, but with discrimination; that is, they do not prescribe them when a person wishes to destroy the embryo because of adultery or out of consideration for youthful beauty, but only to prevent subsequent danger in parturition [childbirth].

"And since it is safer to prevent conception from taking place than to destroy the fetus, we shall now first discourse upon such prevention. For it is much more advantageous not to conceive than to destroy the embryo."[2]

In these excerpts it is obvious that in A.D. 130 one of the greatest of pagan physicians had no medical or ethical scruples against induced abortion or contraception, when medically indicated.

As for Judaism, in Talmudic times (A.D. 200–600) Orthodox Jewry modified its stand in regard to contraception. The Talmud, that great storehouse of post-Biblical law and lore, states that a woman may use contraception on three occasions: when very youthful, when pregnant, and when nursing. This ruling is highly significant. In the first place, the Jewish male was never permitted to use a contraceptive, and in the second place, it indicates that methods of contraception performed by the female were successfully practiced almost two thousand years ago.

The attitude of the Roman Catholic Church remained unmodified until 1930 when Pope Pius XI made the use of the rhythm, or safe period, method of birth control lawful when pregnancy was contraindicated by serious illness of the

[2] Soranus manuscript, *Bibliothèque Nationale*, Paris, France.

mother. In the fourth and fifth decades of this century the position of the Church was further liberalized by statements of Pope Pius XI and Pope Pius XII, legitimatizing the employment of the rhythm technique and timed abstinence by Catholics whenever they deem pregnancy inadvisable. This Church considers the rhythm a natural means for preventing conception and all other techniques unnatural, and therefore wholly illicit. Thus the Catholic and the non-Catholic are in agreement that sexual intercourse without pregnancy as its goal is moral and ethical. The great area of difference is in the methods of contraception that are permissible.

As to abortion (let me state this in passing), the first recognition by a Christian government of the medical wisdom of performing legal abortion, so far as I know, is that of England which passed its first abortion law in 1803. This law, only slightly modified in 1861, is now archaic and in desperate need of revision to fit medicine's progress during the interval. The abortion statutes in each of our fifty states are modeled after their English prototype.

American laws forbidding the dissemination of contraceptives and contraceptive information resulted in large measure from the efforts of Anthony Comstock, a Protestant crusader for the Society for the Suppression of Vice, who in 1873 lobbied through the Congress an "Act for the Suppression of Trade in and Circulation of Obscene Literature and Articles for Immoral Use." Much to the surprise of most of the legislators, the bill they passed included in the catalogue of proscribed obscenities articles and information to prevent conception. The bill was passed in slap-dash fashion—by voice vote in both the House and the Senate, and without debate. The passage of the Comstock law was followed by a "veritable epidemic" of state statutes called "little Comstock Acts."

It took a short time to pass such legislation, but it took sixty-three years to repeal it. The case of the "United States vs. One Package," decided in 1936, is a milestone in the history of the law dealing with contraceptives. Dr. Hannah Stone had imported a package of contraceptive diaphragms from abroad and notified the United States Customs officials, who obliged her with arrest. After much litigation the Circuit Court of Appeals for the Second Circuit, through the majority opinion rendered by Augustus Hand, excluded contraceptives from the law on the basis that they "might intelligently be employed by conscientious and competent physicians for the purpose of saving life or promoting the well-being of their patients."

Forthwith the individual restrictive state statutes were either repealed or fell into disuse, save for the states of Massachusetts and Connecticut. There, they are kept operative by the Catholic majority in the population, egged on by a very vocal priesthood. It is a bit strange and slightly ironical that the Protestants *put* the statutes on the books, and in these two states the Catholics *keep* them on the books in the face of a concerted Protestant effort to repeal them.

After this long historical setting, may I very briefly state my own ethical attitude toward contraception?

First, I cannot see how the use of any harmless method of birth control can be considered unethical, immoral, or irreligious. The Bible was written by brilliant and sincere men, and it is unthinkable to me that its authors would not have modified their views on this subject to serve modern circumstances. There is a strange, irrational tendency to ossify the minds of the great. The fact that Moses or St. Augustine thought thus and so a few hundred or thousand years ago is no guarantee that their opinions about certain things might not be quite different had they lived today. I believe that the great minds of yesteryear would be the wise, rational, and progressive leaders of today. I cannot believe that they would not have considered birth control wholly ethical and moral in the face of the extravagant growth of global population and the pressures of urban existence.

Second, I think thoughtless parenthood is immoral. I believe that the failure to employ reliable methods of contraception during sex relations, if the couple is not emotionally, socially, and physically prepared to become parents, is a grievous wrong.

Third, the giving of contraceptive advice should be wholly democratized so that ability to pay professional fees for such advice should not make the difference between a planned and an unplanned pregnancy. Contraception is a *public-health measure* and like other public-health techniques should be available to all, in every municipal, county, state, and federal health agency. Planned-parenthood clinics should be an anachronism.

Fourth, in our religious and ethical-culture pattern, extramarital sexual relations certainly are not to be condoned. But, considering the matter realistically, they are bound to occur, whether you and I like it or not. And the result of extramarital intercourse, unprotected against pregnancy, is likely to be catastrophic not only for the female participant but particularly for an innocent child so conceived. Under the circumstances I firmly believe that our public, both young people and older, should be educated and enlightened in sex matters, including contraception. I believe our public agencies bear a great responsibility in this connection. With our national illegitimacy rate rising from 5 to 6 per cent, and with a crude estimate of at least one million illegal abortions annually in the United States, this is no time for misguided cautiousness or stilted prudery. Sex education in all its aspects must be furnished in every public and private school and college in the land.

PART II

THERAPEUTIC ABORTION

6

THE DOCTOR'S DILEMMA

PAUL R. KEARNS

Dr. Kearns is a Specialist in Obstetrics and Gynecology, and a Research Associate at Eaton Laboratories in Statesville, North Carolina. He is an officer in the **Reformed Presbyterian Church.**

The sanctity or inviolability of fetal life refers to the rights of the unborn child and constitutes one of the oldest ethical and legal sources of concern. The records of social anthropologists and the earliest medical records indicate that abortion has been practiced since antiquity, and the practice has been complicated by medical uncertainties, human contradictions, varied ethical principles, and conflicting religious beliefs.

The Code of Assyrian Law (1500 B.C.) imposed severe penalties for induced abortion, and the Hebrew Code of Law (Ex. 21:22, 23) stipulated punishment for unintentional traumatic abortion (abortion due to physical injury). The physicians' Hippocratic Oath (about 450 B.C.) sanctimoniously forswears the production of abortion, yet it is recorded that Hippocrates gave advice designed to produce abortion to a musical entertainer who complained of inconvenient pregnancy. Further ethical conflict is encountered when one considers Hippocrates' motives for the admonition against abortion. He belonged to a minority religious group, the Pythagoreans, who held rigorous opinions in sexual matters, even believing that sexual intercourse was justified only for the purpose of producing offspring. They denounced abortion partly because of their religious attitude toward sex and partly to prevent reduction in their ranks.

In classic Greece and Rome abortion was generally regarded with complacency and even commended for eugenic and demographic (population) reasons. Both Plato and Aristotle looked favorably upon abortion as one means of achieving the ideal state. Thus, the Pythagorean doctrine concerning abortion did not reflect the dominant opinion of that era, nor did it exert any significant influence upon our modern attitudes toward abortion.

Moral and legal antipathy to abortion originated with the Hebrews. But it was not until God sent His Son to proclaim the Law of Love that the intrinsic value of the individual was established as a basic part of our religious ethics. It would appear that the commandment, "Thou shalt not kill," would provide a simple basis for moral judgment regarding abortion; however, many centuries of debate by theologians, philosophers, sociologists, and physicians have failed to settle many of the questions on this subject. Construction of a reasonable framework of reference for discussion of some of these questions requires that we define terms, delineate the acceptable medical indications for abortions, and pose the ethical and moral problems that confront us.

Abortion may be defined as the interruption of pregnancy before independent viability (capability of living) of the fetus, and viability is generally considered to occur after about twenty-six to twenty-eight weeks of fetal existence. The term "miscarriage" is the folk word for abortion and has no specific connotation, but common usage associates it only with spontaneous abortion. Abortions may be either spontaneous or artificial.

Spontaneous abortion is the natural process of separation and expulsion of the *conceptus* (embryo and placenta) from the womb and may be compared with the falling of blighted fruit from a tree. It occurs in 12 to 20 per cent of pregnancies due to defects in the ovum, sperm, embryo, or placenta. The following terms describe the condition of pregnancy at various stages of spontaneous abortion: "Threatened abortion" is the term applied to circumstances in which symptoms and signs such as pain and bleeding indicate the possibility of spontaneous abortion; the term "inevitable abortion" indicates that abortion is imminent and not preventable; "incomplete abortion" refers to incomplete separation and expulsion of pregnancy tissue from the womb; "complete abortion" signifies complete separation and expulsion of products of conception from the womb.

Artificial abortion is the separation and expulsion of the *conceptus* by other than natural means, such as medications, trauma (injury), or surgery, and may be legal (therapeutic) or illegal (criminal). Therapeutic abortion is the open and deliberate termination of pregnancy prior to the period of fetal viability because of hazard to the life or health of the mother if pregnancy should continue. Justifiable indications for therapeutic abortion are recognized only when the condition of the mother is such that continuation of the pregnancy would constitute a greater hazard to her life and health than the procedure necessary for interruption of the pregnancy.

In this present discussion we are neither concerned with spontaneous nor criminal abortions because the ethical and moral responsibilities in these instances are quite clear. We are specifically concerned with the difficult ethical and moral decisions on *therapeutic* abortion. These decisions are difficult because our choices are often between delicate shades of gray rather than between black and white.

Medical experience has taught that the association of pregnancy and certain diseases creates a definite danger to the life and health of the mother. It is not possible to make an exact and precise list of these diseases because individual circumstances and severity of disease vary greatly. Also, honest differences of opinion among well-qualified, ethical physicians make it unwise to attempt a didactic approach to the acceptable indications for therapeutic abortion. However, some generalization concerning the indications for therapeutic abortion will help us delineate the boundaries of our thought concerning the moral and ethical implications of this procedure.

Cancer of the pelvic organs of the mother should be treated without regard for the pregnancy because neglect of treatment would surely shorten the life expectancy of the mother and deprive her of a chance for survival. Abortion in such instances is a secondary or indirect result of the obligatory treatment of malignant disease.

While hemorrhage from the womb rarely occurs before the period of fetal viability, its occurrence demands treatment for the control of bleeding regardless of the welfare of the pregnancy. Again, the production of abortion would be an indirect result of necessary treatment of the mother. The same reasoning would apply in the case of ectopic (extra-uterine) pregnancy, whether in the cervix, tubes, or abdominal cavity, because either the presence of hemorrhage or the overwhelming likelihood of hermorrhage would demand prompt and definitive measures for its control or prevention.

The preceding indications for therapeutic abortion offer little difficulty so far as moral or ethical judgment is concerned because no direct action against the embryo or fetus is taken. On the other hand, there are conditions in which deliberate destruction of the pregnancy must be considered. These include such problems as heart disease, hypertension, renal disease, mental diseases, neurologic diseases, etc. Obviously there are different moral and ethical problems posed by this group of diseases. But, first, let us consider the medical problems.

Generally, good medical management of the pregnant patient with heart disease is entirely adequate, and interruption of pregnancy for this condition has become a relatively infrequent necessity. In rare circumstances, however, abortion may be essential to preserve the life and health of the mother.

The decision regarding abortion must rest upon careful and sound evaluation of the disease process and its effects upon the functioning capacity of the patient.

Hypertension is probably the most commonly encountered medical complication. With intelligent use of modern therapy, however, interruption of pregnancy should seldom become necessary. The presence of progressive renal (kidney) vascular disease or the superimposition of acute toxemia (blood poisoning) upon hypertension may create a hazard justifying abortion. Primary renal disease may rarely proceed to progressive deterioration of kidney function and necessitate the termination of pregnancy, and very occasionally a patient may develop unexplained and progressive jaundice during the early months of pregnancy, making abortion a consideration.

Psychiatric conditions may, at times, raise the question of the need for abortion. Such conditions must be carefully evaluated by competent psychiatrists and the effect of pregnancy upon the patient determined. A basic consideration in such circumstances should be the question of possible suicide and the long-term effects upon the ability of the patient to adjust to her role in life. The question of the advisability of therapeutic abortion for a patient who becomes pregnant as a consequence of rape might be included in this group.

Therapeutic abortion is *not* justified for vomiting during pregnancy, for tuberculosis, bronchiectasis, or asthma, because medical treatment offers maximum benefits in the presence of pregnancy. Multiple sclerosis, epilepsy, and leukemia are not influenced by pregnancy and do not offer indications for termination. German measles, Rh blood incompatibility,[1]

[1] Rh blood incompatibility is mentioned several times in this volume. The Rh factor was first found in the red blood cells of the rhesus monkey. Hence the name: Rh—the first two letters of "rhesus." The Rh factor refers to blood types—positive ones and negative. In the case of certain marriages the varying characteristics of the Rh factor do no agree or harmonize, and disease may result in the fetus or baby. The danger of such incompatibility is not too great, but in modern times prospective marriage partners often submit to a blood test. —EDITOR.

previous Caesarean section, and previous fetal abnormalities offer no justification for abortion. Certainly convenience, selfish desires, social and economic reasons never justify abortion.

When therapeutic abortion is considered and decided upon, it should be done as early as possible. Interruption is rarely justified for any reason after the third month of pregnancy because the hazards of the procedure for interruption then become comparable to the risks involved in continuation of the pregnancy. Since there are no safe and effective medications for the satisfactory production of therapeutic abortion and X-ray therapy has many inherent disadvantages, dilatation of the opening of the womb and scraping out the uterine contents is the most effective method of therapeutic abortion if done within the first twelve weeks. Usually abortion after twelve weeks can be accomplished more safely by opening and emptying the uterus through an abdominal incision.

It must be remembered that therapeutic abortion, even when performed under ideal circumstances and by a competent obstetrician-gynecologist, is not without danger. This procedure is not a simple D&C (dilatation and curettage) as is so often thought; it carries with it certain calculated risks. Complications, although rare, may be serious and include such problems as hemorrhage, infection, injury to the womb, thrombophlebitis (inflammation of a clotted vein) and pulmonary embolism (blocking of a blood vessel in the lungs). Late complications of sterility and psycho-sexual problems must be considered, for these do occur.

Legal considerations, while not of primary importance to this discussion, merit a few observations: (1) laws of most states provide for therapeutic abortion when the justified motive for the procedure is the protection of the mother's life; (2) such laws have been broadly interpreted to apply as well to the preservation of the health (including mental health) of the mother; (3) these laws do not consider abortion as homicide.

As previously stated, our modern attitudes toward abortion have as their source the early Christian Church. The condemnation of abortion is based on the premise that abortion is killing and in violation of the commandment, "Thou shalt not kill." The question then arises: When does independent life begin for the embryo or fetus? Theologians have attempted to distinguish between the "formed" and "non-formed" fetus, or between a "living" and "not-yet-living" fetus, or between an "animated" and "not animated" fetus. All these distinctions are concerned with whether a soul has been infused into the body. Roman law derived from Stoic theory the principle that the human soul was infused at the time of birth. Thus, the fetus was considered part of the maternal viscera and not a living human being. Tertullian (A.D. 240), a Roman theologian, called deliberate abortion murder; but only if the fetus had reached a certain stage of development. Augustine (*circa* A.D. 400) made a distinction between the "living" and "not-yet-living" fetus, and the Italian canonist Gratian, in the twelfth century, asked, "Are those who procure abortions to be judged as murderers?" and answered, "He is not a murderer who brings about abortion before the soul is infused into the body." However, there was no agreement regarding the time of animation, and about a century later Thomas Aquinas defined the soul as the first principle of life and stated that life is shown primarily by knowledge and movement. Thus, movement or quickening became the criterion by which presence of life was determined.

Although quickening is a subjective observation, is variable in time of occurrence, and does not denote any specific age or stage of fetal formation, it became accepted by clerics and philosophers, as well as at common law, as a means of distinguishing between the "living" and "not-yet-living" fetus. Blackstone, the eighteenth-century English jurist, stated: "Life begins, in contemplation of law, as soon as the infant is able to stir in the mother's womb." The laws in some of our states still require the presence of fetal movement to establish that termination of pregnancy constitutes the crime of abortion, or they use this criterion for the purpose of determining the degree of punishment for abortion.

The Roman Catholic Church contends that the soul enters the embryo at the moment of conception, and this view is shared by most orthodox Protestants of the present day. Therefore, we find general agreement that life begins at the moment of union of the male and female elements that form the embryo, and the gravity of the sin of abortion is not altered by the duration of gestation. Although the embryo does not possess the qualities of the fully developed human being and does not possess knowledge, it does possess all the inherent potentials of human life and constitutes one phase in human development that continues as an uninterrupted process until physical death intervenes. The time at which a soul is infused into the body or the time when one becomes responsible for moral decisions is not germane to the question of "life."

We must therefore question the moral right of man to determine the relative values of two lives when one is pitted against the other. We must admit that the embryo or fetus has a right to life, but we must also recognize the right of the mother to continued life and health. The basic problem then revolves around the question whether a physician or a group of physicians has the moral right to interfere in the struggle for survival that may exist between a mother and her unborn child.

Concerning the problem of pelvic malignancy or uterine hemorrhage during pregnancy—no tragic moral decision is demanded because moral and ethical responsibility clearly demands the active treatment of the mother without primary concern for the welfare of the fetus. If the saving of the mother's life independently of her pregnant state requires treatment that would cause fetal death as an accessory consequence, such an act could not be considered a direct attempt upon an innocent life. In this regard we might consider the Roman Catholic doctrine of "double effect." For example, the treatment for malignancy or hemorrhage would probably have a double effect—a beneficial effect for the mother and death of the fetus. Provided one does not "will" the bad consequence but only "permits" it to occur, and provided the good consequence is of a positive value equal to or greater than the bad consequence, the act may be morally and ethically permissible.

Other medical indications for therapeutic abortion, such as heart and renal disease, present situations in which direct action must be taken against the fetus. It is in these situations that we face the tragic decisions of compromise, for having recognized the rights of both the fetus and the mother we are confronted with the question whether it is our moral and professional responsibility to make a decision relative to therapeutic abortion.

It is my belief that a Christian physician must assume the professional and moral burden of making these tragic decisions just as he must make difficult decisions concerning the administration of medical treatment, the advisability of a surgical procedure, or the withholding of treatment when calculated risks to the life or health of his patient exist. The position of the physician in such instances may be compared with that of the husband and father who must decide to kill an intruder who intends harm to his family, or the position of a policeman who is faced with the decision of killing an enemy of society who threatens the safety of the community which the policeman has sworn to protect, or the position of a soldier who must kill for the protection of his homeland and loved ones. If it is morally right to kill in any of these instances then it is equally right to perform therapeutic abortion when sound medical judgment determines that the fetus is an aggressor against the mother from whom it takes life. Stating this differently, we might contend that it is right and proper for one to choose the lesser of two evils. To state the physician's responsibility in a more positive manner, it may be emphasized that his first duty is to pursue the course of action that promises to produce the greatest good for his patient. Once he subordinates the claims of the mature patient to the relatively abstract or potential claims of the fetus, he has neglected a primary responsibility.

As Christian people in a Christian society we can and should turn to the ethical teaching of Jesus for enlightenment on any moral or ethical problem. Jesus proclaimed the way men would be and live if they were fully responsive to the rule of God in the realm of God, and in so doing He established the basis for all moral decisions. However, He said little that was explicit about the complexities of human relations. Jesus never minimized the necessity of absolute devotion to God, but to Him fidelity to God was no excuse for naïveté. The Gospel requires of men their best, including the best of strategy. He warned His disciples of the problems they would face in society and suggested that they be "wise as serpents and harmless as doves" (Matt. 10:16). As love for God and one's neighbor is the supreme virtue, so sin is its opposite. Therefore, the motives that lead to a decision for or against therapeutic abortion should emanate from God-centered love for the patient who entrusts herself and her care to the physician. Any act in which one fails to be adequately responsive to the love commandment of Jesus is sinful. The message of Jesus tells us to choose the greater good, and the greater good is that course of action which, in a given circumstance, is relatively the fullest embodiment of faith and love, with God at the center in the act of decision.

Summary and Conclusion

The ethical and moral decisions relative to therapeutic abortion have been discussed, and the moral basis for making decisions may be best stated in the words of an affirmation of The Oxford Conference on "The Universal Church and the World of Nations": "To do what appears as relatively best is an absolute duty before God, and to fail in this is to incur positive guilt."

There are medical circumstances that justify therapeutic abortion, whether it be produced as a direct or indirect consequence of treatment. However, the responsibility for making decisions regarding therapeutic abortion is a weighty matter, requiring personal soul searching by those responsible for such decisions. *One should not sin against conscience.*

Therapeutic abortion should never be thrust upon a patient and her husband, because once they have been informed of the medical opinions they, too, must share in the final decision and the responsibilities that it entails.

Circumstances which require therapeutic abortion in most instances contraindicate future pregnancy. Therefore, sterilization is warranted in most cases. Consequently, the decision for therapeutic abortion requires consideration of the need for sterilization.

Statistics regarding the incidence of therapeutic abortion vary greatly from one hospital to another and from one community to another, and there are also tremendous variations in the medical indications that are cited for this procedure. These facts can only lead to the conclusion that too many pregnancies are interrupted because of laxity in the determination of justifiable indications and deficiencies in personal judgment of the responsible parties.

The decision for therapeutic abortion can only be justified when the motive is pure and honest, and when the physicians making the decisions are exceptionally qualified by both training and judgment to evaluate the problems and arrive at a reasonable decision. Further, this procedure should be decided upon only after adequate consultations by competent men, and should then be done openly in a hospital where the activities of individual staff members are scrutinized by the staff organization.

All life is sacred to the truly ethical physician, and he

makes distinctions only as each case comes before him and under the pressure of necessity for deciding which of two lives must be sacrificed in order to preserve the life and health of the other.

7

ABORTION AND THE
CHRISTIAN CONSCIENCE

Hammell Pierce Shipps

> **Dr. Shipps** is Assistant Professor of Clinical Ob-
> stetrics and Gynecology at Jefferson Medical Col-
> lege in Philadelphia. He is also Chief Gynecologist
> at Cooper Hospital, Camden, New Jersey, and
> Zurbrugg Hospital, Riverside, New Jersey. Church
> connection: **Evangelical Christian.**

Therapeutic abortion may be defined as the
interruption of human pregnancy with legal justification,
prior to viability (capability of living) of the fetus.

Permissibility and Indications

Legal justification of abortion is defined in most states of
the United States as the right of a doctor to terminate a pregnancy when in his honest opinion this step is necessary to
preserve the life of the mother. Legal justification is not defined in the statutes of New Jersey, Pennsylvania, and Massachusetts. A few states allow that abortion may be performed
to preserve the *health* as well as the *life* of the mother.

Dr. E. D. Brothers, an expert in medical law, makes the
following comment: "The necessity mentioned in the various
statutes, and which as a matter of common law will justify
the operation, is intended to cover only those cases where the
death of the mother might reasonably be expected to result
from natural causes, growing out of or aggravated by pregnancy, unless the child is destroyed. Of course it need not

appear that the death of the mother is inevitable and at hand in the absence of the operation."[1]

There are, to my knowledge, no legal provisions, in any of the states, for abortion in cases of rape, illegitimacy, or for economic, social, or eugenic reasons, or for possible abnormalities of the fetus (such as, for example, in the recent thalidomide cases). On the other hand, there is no legal *prevention* of such abortions except through action in the civil courts.

In the case of a lawful, or therapeutic, abortion, consultation with another physician is demanded by the statutes of many states. It is required that at least two qualified physicians agree that the abortion is necessary. This is also a requirement in all accredited hospitals in the United States.

Detailed listing of indications is practically impossible because each patient is an individual and special problem. Also, medical progress in the case of patients has been such that many previous indications for abortion are no longer valid.

Incidence

It has been estimated that about 18,000 therapeutic abortions are performed in the United States annually. There has been a decline in frequency during the past two decades. In 1943 there were 5.1 per 1,000 live births; in 1953, 2.9 per 1,000 live births. During that period the organic indications decreased from 4.7 to 1.7, while the psychiatric indications increased. In 1943 psychiatric indications accounted for 8 per cent of the cases, while in 1953 these indications accounted for 40 per cent.

Recent statistical studies in New York City indicate a marked difference in incidence, depending upon race, social status, and type of hospital service. In 1943 there were 5.1 therapeutic abortions per 1,000 live births; in 1959 there

[1] E. D. Brothers, *Medical Jurisprudence*, C. B. Mosby Co., St. Louis, 1930.

were 2.1 per 1,000 live births. The figures for 1957–59 suggest that there must be a dual standard of permissiveness, for the rate of the white population (2.9) was nearly five times that in the Negro (0.6), and nearly ten times that in the Puerto Rican (0.3). And the rate in private hospitals was 5.2, in the voluntary and teaching hospitals 1.9, and in the county and city hospitals 0.4 per 1,000 live births. During the period reported there had been a marked decline in the medical indications, a marked rise in the psychiatric indications (accounting for 62 per cent of the abortions), and a considerable rise in those cases performed because of viral diseases in the mother (especially Rubella) during early pregnancy (12.6 per cent).[2]

Statistics such as these should make us evaluate performance in the light of ethics and integrity. Why should there be such a marked difference in these various groups?

To the Christian physician each individual life that comes under his care is a sacred trust. This intensifies his concern and brings the Christian conscience into the picture when considering indication for abortion.

Some may ask whether a Christian physician is ever justified in recommending or performing an abortion. Scripture says: "Thou shalt not kill." But remember, this injunction can be applied with equal warrant or lack of warrant to capital punishment and to warfare. One must also remember that in any given case one might be indirectly responsible for the death of the mother of a family by not terminating her pregnancy, and such a death might occur before the fetus is viable, and thus both lives might be sacrificed. The moral responsibility in *recommending* abortion is of course the same as in the performance of abortion.

There are some questions revolving around the matter of therapeutic abortion that are difficult to answer. Should the

[2] Edwin M. Gold, *Changing Indications for Therapeutic Abortion*, *Audio-Digest Obs.*, Vol. 8, No. 10.

indications be extended to include the prevention of serious impairment of the physical or mental health of the mother? Should abortion be used to prevent the birth of an infant damaged by irremediable hereditary or congenital conditions? What should be done if a wife or daughter is pregnant as a result of rape?

The increasing number of therapeutic abortions being done for psychiatric reasons raises the question whether or not in many instances these are valid and legal indications, or if pressures arising out of socio-economic and other situations are not the real basis for the procedure. The threat of suicide on the part of a woman carrying an undesired pregnancy is rarely a valid indication. Statistics indicate that such threats are rarely carried out. And abortion itself is likely to have a serious psychological effect upon the mother unless she knows there was an adequate medical reason for the termination of her pregnancy. Guilt, hostility, and frustration are likely consequences.

Socio-economic conditions for therapeutic abortion are excluded in United States laws. However, as mentioned above, such conditions may be at the root of many cases referred to the psychiatrist, and because the mother has threatened suicide therapeutic abortion is recommended. In the light of statistics, can such be morally justified? I think not.

The law says abortion may be performed to save the life of the mother. Morally, may it not be expressed as follows: If we do not abort, or have the patient aborted, and the mother dies as a result of the pregnancy, we are responsible for her death. There may be sins of omission as well as sins of commission.

The problem of evaluation is rarely an easy one. It is always the physician's duty to preserve and save life, whenever possible. To destroy human life deliberately is repugnant to the Christian conscience. To recommend abortion is, in a sense, to admit defeat. And the outcome, if abortion is not done, cannot always be known with certainty. With our human limitations it is not always possible to perform perfectly. But as Christians we can set for ourselves certain standards. We should strive to be intellectually honest and morally upright. Our standards should be uniform from case to case, and each case should be carefully weighed in the light of all possible accumulated information, and thus an attempt should be made to reach an unbiased decision. And I need not remind our Christian physicians that the Scripture says, "If any of you lack wisdom, let him ask of God, who giveth to all men liberally . . . and it shall be given him." (Jas. 1:5)

While in the light of modern advances in medicine organic disease should rarely be an indication for the termination of pregnancy, such situations do arise. It then becomes necessary to save the life of the mother. But there is also the possibility on some such occasions that the operation for termination of pregnancy may be as serious in its consequences as continuation of the pregnancy under carefully controlled conditions. This may apply particularly to some cases of cardiovascular disease or pulmonary tuberculosis, either of which under modern treatment may improve during pregnancy.

There is an occasional case of severe toxemia. [A morbid or poisoned state of the blood. —Editor.] during the early months of pregnancy that is refractory to treatment, and termination of pregnancy is then required to save the life of the mother. Uncontrolled hemorrhage from placenta previa also demands termination of pregnancy to save the mother. The same applies to pregnancy in the Fallopian tube or in the rudimentary horn of a bicornuate (double-horned) uterus.

Pregnancy occurring in a woman with malignant disease, or malignant disease discovered during the course of pregnancy, presents problems for careful study, individualization, and management. The problem is too involved for adequate discussion in this chapter. Each case presents a somewhat varied problem.

The occurrence of certain virus diseases in the mother during the early months of pregnancy has been shown to produce a higher than normal incidence of malformed babies. Rubella (German measles) is at present at the top of this list. The earlier such a disease occurs during the first three months of pregnancy, the higher is the likely incidence of malformation. Occurrence after the fourth month of pregnancy apparently has no effect upon this incidence. This has caused so much concern upon the part of some parents and physicians that therapeutic abortion has been recommended. But the problem here is that not all of these babies are malformed. We can rarely if ever tell which ones are affected. And in many of those affected the malformation is not incompatible with a relatively normal life. So, if such is to be considered an indication for abortion, a large number of normal babies (perhaps 70 per cent) will be sacrificed. In the present state of our knowledge about this condition this appears to be a morally unjustifiable indication for abortion. And who are we to judge? A baby born totally blind might be another Helen Keller or a Fannie Crosby.

In some countries of the world—Russia and Japan for example—there has been a marked liberalization of the abortion laws, so that abortions can be performed upon proper request, without medical indication. This situation is of course intolerable to the Christian conscience. The Christian concept of the sacredness of life demands that the physician feel that, when he recommends termination of pregnancy before the time of viability of the fetus, he do so to save or preserve the mother's life. He is not infallible and may err in judgment, and at times great pressures may be brought to bear upon him, but his aim must be to keep his conscience clear before God and man.

Prophylaxis

One of the aims of medical practice is to prevent as well as to treat disease. It seems that prevention has a place in the consideration of therapeutic abortion.

Our aim should be to improve the health of mothers and

to eradicate or control diseases that might be so affected by pregnancy as to indicate abortion. Active or passive immunity against viral diseases may protect against malformations. Great progress has been made, and is still being made, along these lines. At times diseases adversely affected by pregnancy may not be discovered before pregnancy has occurred, but even here therapy and improvement, or even cure, may be accomplished without interruption of pregnancy.

Those women who would be so affected by pregnancy as to make therapeutic abortion necessary should use appropriate measures to prevent conception. We recognize that at times there may be flaws in this practice.

Conclusion

Therapeutic abortion is contrary to ideal medical practice, which is dedicated to the preservation of life. There are occasions when its performance becomes necessary to preserve the life of the mother. Legitimate incidence should become less and less with the advance in medical science. The Christian should face this problem in the light of his relationship to God and his obligation to his fellow man.

8

THE PHYSICIAN AND THE
SIXTH COMMANDMENT

Gordon E. Maxwell

Dr. Maxwell, a Protestant, is a Specialist in Obstetrics and Gynecology at the Salina Clinic in Salina, Kansas.

Abortion concerns the termination of a pregnancy before the fetus has developed sufficiently to survive extra-uterine existence. This includes essentially all pregnancies of less than twenty-eight weeks of gestation and all fetuses of thirty-four ounces or less in weight, although rare exceptions occur.[1]

Abortion may be spontaneous, i.e., due to natural causes, or induced by voluntary activity of the gravid (pregnant) woman or her assistants. Induced abortions are generally considered in two classes, therapeutic or criminal, which implies that all induced abortions are either part of a necessary medical treatment or are contrary to law. Perhaps a more realistic dichotomy (division into two classes) to apply to a situation requiring refined medical judgment and moral evaluation would be *indicated* or *elective;* and it is in the distinction between these two categories that wide variations occur among different cultures and religions. At present the attitudes on indication vary from the one extreme of "there are no indica-

[1] Nicholson J. Eastman, *Williams' Obstetrics,* 10th ed., Appleton-Century-Crofts, New York, 1950.

tions" (frequently attributed, incorrectly, to the Roman Catholic Church) to the concept of elective maternity or "free all women from unwanted conceptions."

In this brief discussion the theological, legal, and medical aspects of induced abortion will be presented and correlated. The critical issue in induced abortion for a Christian concerns the question when a human *conceptus* receives a human soul; thence, when an abortion ceases to be mere removal of tissue and becomes murder and, therefore, a breach of the sixth commandment. The lawmaker must decide on the questions of extending legal protection to the helpless, and of having the support of society in enforcing this protection. The physician seeks to reconcile his precept of the preservation of life with the occasional need, or with the importunity of the patient, to interrupt intra-uterine life. Neither a review of the historic legacy of mankind nor an evaluation of current opinion will provide unequivocal or definitive solutions to these questions.

A Glimpse of the Past

Ancient societies were apparently permissive regarding induced abortion, seeing knowledge of techniques is evidenced in ancient Chinese and Egyptian writings.[2] Assyrian[3] and Old Testament Hebrew laws[4] assess penalties upon those who cause abortion. The ancient Greeks paid attention to eugenics and population control, and reached the conclusion that infanticide (Plato) or abortions (Aristotle) would be helpful in these areas.[5] The stern and ascetic Pythagoreans dissented,

[2] S. H. Boulas, R. W. Preucel, and J. H. More, *Obstetrical and Gynecological Survey,* 19:223, 1962.
[3] Nicholson J. Eastman, Editorial, *Obstetrical and Gynecological Survey,* 13:503 ff., 1958.
[4] Bible, Exod. 21:22.
[5] Glanville Williams, *The Sanctity of Life and the Criminal Law,* Alfred A. Knopf, Inc., New York, 1957.

and from them we have inherited the physicians' Hippocratic oath with its interdiction of abortion.

The early Christian theologians, relatively ignorant of embryonal physiology, believed that the fetus became a living person with a soul when quickening, which is the onset of detectable fetal motion, had occurred. Tertullian, third-century theologian, therefore declared that abortion of the *animated* fetus was illicit. Likewise, Thomas Aquinas, beloved Aristotelian of ten centuries later, reasoned that the soul is the first principle of life; that life is evidenced by knowledge or movement; with the conclusion that life commences with fetal motion and not with conception; and, therefore, that abortion prior to quickening does not involve the loss of human life.

During the nineteenth century the distinction between conception and animation was dropped in Roman Catholic theology. This Church now teaches that animation, with Divine creation and infusion of the soul, occurs at conception, and that the fertilized ovum is considered to be a human person.[6,7]

The conclusion which Roman Catholic theologians derive from this concept is this: if a gravida's (pregnant woman's) life is threatened by a genital disorder which must be treated, this treatment may be undertaken even though it will have the secondary undesired effect of terminating the pregnancy; but if the gravida's life is threatened by failure of some other organ system, and the physician wishes to decrease the burden on the damaged organ by terminating the pregnancy with a direct abortion, this is not permissible. This distinction is based on the principle of the "double effect," which is the acceptance of an unwanted secondary result of an action that has a beneficial primary aim.

[6] G. Kelly, *Medico-Moral Problems,* The Catholic Hospital Association of the United States and Canada, St. Louis, 1948.

[7] John Marshall, *Medicine and Morals,* Hawthorn Books, New York, 1960.

Present-day Trends

At the present time there are four rather distinct trends in belief and action on induced abortion. There are those who feel that direct abortion is almost never legitimate; those who consider it to be a medical last resort for seriously ill patients; those who feel that the needs of the mother are primary, and the fetus is very secondary; and finally those who would free women of all unwanted conceptions.

Foremost in the "almost-never" group are members of the Roman Catholic Church, whose firm teaching is that direct destruction of the embryo is a sin punishable by excommunication. But four specific medical exceptions are allowed by this Church's principle of "double effect":

1. To control disastrous uterine hemorrhage, the uterus may be evacuated or removed.

2. Invasive cancer of the cervix may be irradiated, although death of the fetus will inevitably occur.

3. If the uterus is so diseased that it requires immediate removal during pregnancy, this may be done.

4. To prevent or control bleeding from ectopic (extra-uterine) gestations, as in tubal pregnancy, the damaged tissue with its enclosed embryo may be removed.

The second group, which countenances induced abortion to protect the life of the seriously ill patient, includes most conservative American physicians and is embodied in law by most of the states. These physicians would add to the above-mentioned indications the following:

1. Patients whose diseased cardiovascular system markedly restricts normal activity should not be subjected to the known cardiovascular burden of preg-

nancy. This situation is commonly due to rheumatic heart disease with valvular lesions, less often to congenital or hypertensive cardiovascular disease.

2. In patients who have failing kidney reserve, as the postnephrectomy patient with pyelonephritis, death can be prevented or delayed by a therapeutic abortion.

3. The elderly diabetic with nephritis or vascular disease should not continue her pregnancy.

4. Most physicians[8] believe that the patient under treatment for cancer of the breast should be aborted.

5. Beyond these indications is one large group that appears in all statistical studies: psychiatric indications. The patient who threatens suicide if her pregnancy is not terminated may be dangerous to herself or may only be seeking to be aborted. This group of patients is very difficult to assess and medical thinking differs widely on the question.

The tenor of the most recent studies in medical literature is remarkably consistent.[9] They criticize the indication formerly accepted and note with satisfaction a declining incidence based on improved medical care, and conclude with a confident expression of hope that this declining trend will continue.

The medical validity of this body of opinion is based on the physicians' code, or belief in the preservation of life. Physiologically, there can be no doubt but that the fertilized ovum has life, with ability to grow and develop into a recognizable human person. There is no other event in human

[8] H. K. Miller, *American Journal of Obstetrics and Gynecology,* 83:607, 1962.

[9] See *Obstetrical and Gynecological Survey,* 19:223, 1962; 17:168, 1961; 11:323, 1958. Also, A. S. Majury, *American Journal of Obstetrics and Gynecology,* 82:10, 1961.

development which reasonably could be postulated to represent the onset of life. Implantation in the uterus occurs at one week; all organ systems are initiated by four weeks; detectable fetal motion occurs at eighteen to twenty weeks; and the fetus is capable of extra-uterine life at about twenty-eight weeks. There are important milestones in fetal development, but, as stated, none can be postulated as the incipient point of fetal existence.

This concept of human origin coincides with the conservative Christian view that the developing embryo embodies a soul created by God, and that for that reason the embryo should be destroyed only from direst necessity, namely, when failure to do so would jeopardize the survival of both mother and fetus.

The third body of opinion is expressed by those who concede that life exists in the embryo, but that it is primitive, unconscious, insensate, dependent life whose right to continued development is definitely secondary to the needs of the mother and of society. This view is brilliantly and sympathetically expressed in medicine by Alan F. Guttmacher,[10] in law by Glanville Williams,[11] and is being rather widely practiced in Sweden, Norway, and Denmark.[12, 13]

This group would extend the above-mentioned medical indications to include psychoneurosis, anxiety, malnutrition, obesity, multiparity (too many children), and fatigue. It would add mental deficiency, congenital anomalies, and maternal rubella (German measles) as eugenic indications to help eliminate defective offspring. Lastly, it would free the mothers of unwanted pregnancies due to rape, incest, and some circumstances of illegitimacy.

[10] Quoted by E. M. and S. M. Duvall, *Sexways in Fact and Faith*, Association Press, New York, 1961.
[11] See footnote 5.
[12] P. Arn, *Acta Obst. and Gynec. Scandin.* 37, Supplement 1, 1958.
[13] P. Kolstad, *Obstetrical and Gynecological Survey*, 13:50s, 1958.

Guttmacher believes that our present restrictive attitudes are unfair to the patients mentioned in the categories above, and that legal abortion would greatly decrease suffering and illness among these patients. Mr. Williams believes that the present abortion laws are failing, as evidenced by the high incidence of illicit abortions, with very few legal penalties being inflicted. Laws, he feels, are enforceable only if society believes them to be necessary and just, and society at present does not condemn early induced abortions very strongly. He concludes that a reformed law should consider a pregnancy to be basically the concern of the mother. If she wishes to have it terminated by abortion she should be legally free to do so. He does not say that this would be a morally correct law, but that it would be a socially valid and legally usable one. As a step in this direction, he proposes legal abortion along the lines sketched out above.

The Scandinavian countries have enacted liberal legislation embodying the indications described. Their legal abortion rate is now about fifty per 1,000 live births, compared with three to five per 1,000 in the United States. Although there is pressure both to restrict and to liberalize the Scandinavian laws, they are thought by many to be fairly satisfactory except for one weakness: the criminal abortion rate still equals or exceeds that of the legal abortions.

The last body of current thought suggests that no woman should be burdened with an unwanted gestation and should be free to have it terminated by competent operators in good facilities. It is thought, and probably correctly, that this is the only way in which the dangerous and costly practice of criminal abortion can be controlled. It was for this reason that the Soviet Union and other eastern European countries liberalized their abortion law to this ultimate extent.[14] Japan has virtually followed suit, although that country's present legal

[14] C. Tietze and H. Lehfeldt, *Jama* 175:1149; 1961.

abortion rate, 1,050 against 1,000 live births, is partly achieved by a free interpretation of the existing law. This is accepted by the Japanese Government as an efficacious means of population control.

This very liberal view can be criticized from several angles. Its chief advantage would lie in the obvious fact that in order to compete with and eliminate the criminal abortionist, legalized medical abortion would have to provide better service.

The Christian Ethic

Out of this welter of differing historic and contemporary attitudes, can we derive a logical, consistent, practical ethic for the Christian physician? To me these facts seem self-evident:

1. The life of the fetus commences with conception; from this point on, in the care of the pregnant patient, we have two lives to protect.

2. Willful destruction of innocent persons is contrary to Christian ethics, moral law, and the inclination of decent people.

3. The only acceptable exception to this principle would be when failure to interrupt a pregnancy would result in the *probable* loss of both lives. In these rather rare cases, previously described, it is preferable to sacrifice the fetus rather than to tolerate the fairly certain death of both. The degree of probability of maternal death if the pregnancy continues should be ascertained in consensus by a team of careful, conscientious physicians.

It would be unwise if not impracticable to seek to compel everyone to conform to Christian moral judgment in this area, but the Christian believer who is compelled to advise or decide on this vital question should have valid and consistent reasons for his decisions.

9

THERAPEUTIC ABORTION
SELDOM NECESSARY

R. Dale Hunsaker

Dr. Hunsaker, a **Protestant,** is a Specialist in Obstetrics and Gynecology at the Permanente Clinic in Portland, Oregon.

The words abortion and miscarriage are practically synonymous, although some physicians make somewhat of a distinction between the two. We shall use the word abortion, which means the interruption or termination of a pregnancy at any stage of gestation before the fetus has attained a stage or age of viability (capability of living outside of the uterus). There is no agreement in medical circles at just which period of gestation this stage of viability has been reached, but the majority of medical scientists agree that it is at some time before twenty weeks of gestation have been completed.

There are different types of abortion. Let us name them and describe them with just a handful of words:

Spontaneous abortion is the termination of a pregnancy through natural causes, without the use of mechanical or chemical agents.

Induced abortion is brought on by the use of mechanical or chemical agents, and is either therapeutic or criminal.

Therapeutic abortion is one in which a pregnancy is brought to an end because it is felt that its continuation would be very hazardous, or even cause the mother's death, or when there is some proof that a malformed child or mentally deficient child will be delivered.

Criminal abortion is the termination of a pregnancy without medical or legal justification. This term is used loosely to include also the period beyond the twenty weeks of uterine gestation.

Complete abortion is one in which the entire product of conception has been expelled.

Incomplete abortion is one in which only part of the product has been expelled and some of the gestational tissue remains within the uterus.

Missed abortion signifies that the fetus died in the uterus and was retained therein for a period of sixty days or longer.

Habitual abortion describes the condition of a woman in which she has had three or more consecutive pregnancies terminate spontaneously as abortions.

Psychic abortion denotes an experience in which there was tentative proof that a spontaneous abortion occurred as the result of psychic shock. However, there is still too little concrete evidence to make this a fixed classification.

Tubal abortion is the process in which the fertilized ovum, or egg, attaches itself to the inner lining of the Fallopian tube, and then is later extruded through the fimbriated end of the tube into the peritoneal cavity (abdominal cavity). There are cases on record which have gone to full term when a tubal abortion occurred. These have become what are known as abdominal pregnancies, and they represent a very grave obstetrical condition.

When considering the subject of therapeutic abortion one must take into consideration that many states legalize such abortion to protect a woman's health and to preserve her life. But we must also remember that when these antiquated laws were enacted pregnancy was still a relatively dangerous experience for the woman. Through the years medical advances have done much to make pregnancy a much safer experience for both the mother and her baby. It is rarely necessary these days to perform a therapeutic abortion to save a life. The previously high maternal and infant death rate has dropped tremendously in recent years. Obstetrics is nearing its goal.

In deciding whether a patient should have a therapeutic abortion because the life of the mother is endangered we must of course consider the more serious diseases such as rheumatic heart disease, uncontrollable diabetes, chronic pyelonephritis (inflammation of a kidney and its pelvis), and the like. But we must not be led astray by the pregnant mother's mental aberrations, if any. Many pregnant women experience very bizarre likes and dislikes and behavior patterns during pregnancy. These women, at the worst, need only psychiatric help and not a therapeutic abortion.

In this connection I am recalling specifically a patient whom I delivered a few months ago, and who, upon finding out that she was pregnant, had gone with her husband to seek the advice of a psychiatrist in regard to a therapeutic abortion. The psychiatrist heartily recommended an abortion on the basis that the child's first few years of life would be rather unstable. She was sent to see an obstetrician who concurred with this dubious piece of advice. After I got a chance to discuss this with them it was felt that this was all irrational thinking, because the first few years, if not all the years, of anyone's life are filled with uncertainties and instability. I succeeded in making them realize that this unborn child of theirs had as much right to live in this "unstable" world of ours as any of us "grownups." This young woman carried her infant to term and had an uneventful delivery. After all was done and over the situation was rediscussed. As she looked back, she realized how utterly ridiculous the thought had been to want a therapeutic abortion. She realized that, in her mental confusion after learning that she was pregnant, she was definitely irrational in making the request for an abortion. They are now a very happy family.

It is my belief that in the matter of childbearing many of our American women could with great benefit use a good supply of old-fashioned stamina. On the Lewis and Clark expedition, as the reader may recall, Sacagawea stopped and delivered her own infant and then caught up with the expedition and came on to the Oregon country with them. I certainly do not advocate this sort of thing, but it does raise a question in one's mind as to the weakness of the present-day man, woman, and family.

Illegitimacy is rising in the United States. There has been an increase of approximately 14 per cent in the last ten years. Yet the United States' illegitimacy rate is among the lowest in the world. This is no doubt due to our historic religious beliefs and the social and economic levels we have been able to attain. We find that the colored population of South Africa has the highest rate, which is to be expected considering their degrees of intelligence and education, as well as their social patterns and economic level. But, as stated, the United States is slipping fast. Biblical religion is losing its hold on the general public. Whether this is due to a lessening or weakening of Biblical teaching on the part of ministers and priests, these churchmen themselves have to decide. Personally it looks to this writer as though illegitimacy is keeping pace with the process of liberalization in religious believing and thinking. This does not mean, however, that officially the Churches are getting more liberal about premarital intercourse. They certainly are not. The trouble seems to lie in the ranks: certain teaching elements and certain elements among the general church membership.

At one time words like syphilis, gonorrhea, and even sex were taboo in our speech and as a topic brought up in social circles for discussion. Today these subjects are being discussed at random. Perhaps this openness and outspokenness have not only led to a better-informed public but also to a higher rate of promiscuity. And many authorities feel that modern dress, or rather "no dress," has much to do with society's acceptance of a greater sexual liberality. In the Book of Genesis we find that the Lord himself provided fallen man with adequate clothing to cover his nakedness. The Lord of course had a very solid reason for this action. Today clothing is becoming very scanty, very minimal. There seems to be a regular drive to expose as much of the body as possible—to show one's wares much as a peddler on the street shows his wares to the passing prospective customers.

As the illegitimacy rate rises, so will the criminal abortion rate. And while we have laws to curtail the so-called professional abortionists, these individuals are rarely convicted in spite of the fact that the laws are being knowingly violated. One main reason for this slackness in law enforcement is of course the fact that the people who seek the abortionists' services seek with equal or greater zeal to avoid publicity.

One of the most painful decisions for an obstetrician to make is whether to advise, and then perform, a therapeutic abortion. Hospitals have their own accepted procedure for control of this act of destruction (which has by some religions, certain courts, and a number of sensational journalists been labeled as murder). Some consider a fertilized ovum as having a soul, and the intra-uterine gestational period as one phase of life, the extra-uterine period on earth as another phase, and the unknown hereafter, called eternity, or heaven or hell, still another phase. On this thought one can only philosophize.

Still, there never was a time or place in history in which criminal law was more disregarded or violated than right here and now—by the so-called professional abortionists. As to men of high reputation and ethics in the medical profession, the situation is made difficult by the fact that the state legislatures do not definitely outline what constitutes the legal difference beween a criminal and a therapeutic abortion. Most states allow a therapeutic abortion after proper consultation with other physicians. Even then there is the possibility of litigation. Many hospitals have a therapeutic-abortion committee, but such a committee, also, is not a perfect barrier against litigation. The decision in a case of therapeutic abortion must rest on the indefinite laws of the state, accepted medical practices and ethics, and, especially, the attending physician's own feelings regarding the rightness or wrongness of the act.

No law or medical ethics permit a therapeutic abortion to be done in cases where pregnancy results from forcible rape, incest, illegitimacy, or poverty. As to rape, it is felt by many that the incidence of forcible rape is not as high as the court records show. American men are great believers in showing gallantry to women; they have put women on a pedestal; they'll usually take a woman's word any time against a man's —also in the courts. As a matter of fact, however, women are no more saintly than men are. Charges of rape are often pressed in courts when the woman is as guilty as the man, and all the "victim" is after is a good financial settlement. There are other, similar motivations. I recall a statement made to me by a very prominent obstetrician friend of mine about cases of rape. "All rape," he said, "is not rape. It is a lot easier for a woman to run with her dress pulled up than it is for a man to run with his pants down." This was putting it a bit coarsely—he could be that way at times—but it reflects a situation far from fictional. At the same time it must be admitted that there are genuine cases of rape. A physician must search his own conscience very thoroughly when presented with the question of whether or not to suggest an abortion of a married woman impregnated by proved rape, and after the rapist is convicted. What to do in such a case? The Bible Book of Ecclesiastes says, "To everything there is a season, and a time for every purpose under the heaven: A time to be born and a time to die. . . ." (Eccl. 3:1, 2) And the same Bible tells us that God alone has the right to determine the hour of death. In my opinion a case such as I have referred to belongs to what ancient scholars used to call "cases of conscience." My own conscience would not permit any interference with the development of the fetus, if conditions seemed favorable. I have a profound reverence for human life, even in its incipiency, and I do not believe in doing away with a human embryo that is developing into a human baby and is en route to be born. I do not believe in it, regardless of the circumstances. Human intelligence, judgment, and love would find a solution to what would admittedly be a very painful problem.

And then there is the so-called population explosion. The present live-birth rate in the United States is approximately 4,330,000 per annum, and shows a progressive increase to about 6,000,000 by 1970, and perhaps 7,000,000 by 1975. India is producing in the neighborhood of 16,000,000 live babies a year, and it seems that that country's rate of increase in births will hardly be changed—certainly not in the immediate future. Other parts of the world are in much the same situation. Is therapeutic abortion, among other means and measures, indicated to counteract this immense growth? Most certainly not! The necessary countermeasures lie in the fields of sterilization and contraception. But other writers for this symposium are taking care of those subjects. That something thorough and extensive has to be done in this matter of population explosion goes without saying.

Speaking of our own country, I feel we are definitely oversexed. With too many people, and for the greater part of their lives, sex is the be-all and end-all of existence. It is the axis around which their social life, artistic efforts, recreational activities, entertainment, keep spinning and spinning, interminably. Mere children are being caught up in the swirl, by the hundreds of thousands. Prematrimonial and matrimonial morals have in countless cases gone out the window. And there is nothing so desperately necessary in these circumstances as a serious preaching, in the name of the all-sovereign God, of the basic morals that were the framework of our social and national structure in our real heyday.

In the meantime, there are consultation centers available

for education of the public. This education must be aimed especially at sex instruction for children at a level which is understandable to them, giving them full information on planned parenthood and abortions, listing the advantages, disadvantages, consequences, etc. Because of the shortage of doctors in the United States—a shortage that will not be remedied in the years immediately ahead—the medical profession cannot assume leadership in a campaign for sex education and preparation for marriage. But other professionals can, and should, take the lead.

The promiscuous use of contraceptives is of course never the answer in our present-day moral maelstrom. On more occasions than I care to recall I have been approached by the young, single girl requesting contraceptive devices or tablets. The giving of these is neither moral nor right. It would mean only one thing: that I approve of and use my medical knowledge and ability to help her carry on with her illicit sexual activities. This I cannot do because of my religious beliefs and the teachings of Scripture, and because, from a medical standpoint, the rate of venereal disease is bound to keep pace with the rate of promiscuity. And the rate of venereal disease in the young teen-ager in the United States today is appalling.

Getting back to our subject proper, in my twelve years of doing obstetrics and gynecology I have yet to see the patient whose life I felt would be lost if she carried an already conceived and developing pregnancy. So the occasion for drastic action is not a very frequent one. I feel that a therapeutic abortion for the saving of the mother's life is seldom indicated —and this is the only reason for doing an abortion that the law permits. Nor should this legal permission ever become a cloak behind which to hide.

It is true that many mothers are damaged irreparably by carrying a pregnancy. But that does not mean that their lives are endangered—neither *their* lives nor those of their babies. And I am sure that when these critical decisions do present themselves, that all physicians, Christian and non-Christian alike, are doing a lot of thinking, and even praying in their own way, before deciding what can and should be done.

As for Christian physicians—the Great Physician knows of these crucial instances and will lead us to the right decisions if we will only ask and wait for Him.

10

WHEN A MOTHER'S LIFE IS AT STAKE—ACT

Albert C. Hirshfield

> **Dr. Hirshfield** is a Specialist in Obstetrics and Gynecology. He practices in Oklahoma City, Oklahoma, and is a **Protestant.**

In making these few comments on therapeutic abortion I am assuming that other writers on this subject have sufficiently covered the ground of abortion in general, so that it will not be necessary for me to lay the groundwork for this specific subject. May I say in all humility that I consider it my good fortune to have practiced medicine along this particular line for half a century, and that during that time I have not only carefully watched obstetrical medicine develop to its present remarkable stage but have personally sought to make assiduous use of such new findings as seemed warranted.

As the word "therapeutic" suggests, this type of abortion may be done only in the genuine interest of the mother's health, or even her very life. It may be done (1) as a direct means to save the mother's life, (2) to eliminate a condition which may threaten her life, and (3) to avoid certain dangers which may supervene if pregnancy is allowed to progress to full term. While it is considered a last resort operation, the physician bears the heavy responsibility of not postponing the operation until it is too late to save the mother's life. I have personally seen cases in which, because of a natural desire to try every known procedure, or because of disagreement between physician and consultants, or because of a reluctance on the part of the patient or her family, the operation was done too late to save the patient's life.

At the outset, let me say that in no case a decision to terminate pregnancy should have a social or economic basis. The basis must be purely medical. Like most physicians in this field, I have been besieged any number of times by couples seeking an abortion because they already have a large family, or because of relative poverty, or inability to feed, clothe, and educate another child. My answer to this is invariably that we can readily find a good home for the baby, with all the advantages. This is seldom accepted. While I am a firm believer in birth control in such cases, I cannot condone an abortion if pregnancy occurs, as there are always countless childless couples very eager to help out in such circumstances.

The physician owes the patient, society and, above all, God, the solemn duty of considering a therapeutic abortion where serious disease complicates pregnancy. He must seriously and prayerfully examine his conscience as to the necessity and morality of an abortion. If in doubt (and he owes the mother the benefit of the doubt) he should call in another physician. If he happens to be a relatively young physician, it is best for him to call in an older and more experienced man. Before the final act consultation is required by ethics and law, and many hospitals now require the written assent of two consultants.

Many women beg for an abortion because of conditions less serious than major illness, or because some physician has advised them never to have another baby. My answer in these cases is that, if they will secure a written recommendation for an abortion from two reputable and experienced doctors of medicine, I will consider the matter. That usually ends the proceeding. Even physicians who forbid future pregnancies are not willing to get out on a limb except in the case of really serious complications. To women who *insist* on an abortion because some physician somewhere has told them that a pregnancy would be "very serious" I suggest that they go back to that physician.

While there are still many conditions which in their more serious aspects may call for a therapeutic abortion, the list has shrunk very materially in the fifty years I have practiced. This is due to the improved understanding and treatment of these conditions and the life-saving efficiency of the well-equipped modern hospital. On the other hand, there is much more latitude in the matter of inducing necessary premature labor, for after viability and with the use of incubators and modern pediatric care most babies of six months or longer can be saved. Of course, the nearer full term the better the chance for survival of the infant. Any infant weighing two and a half pounds or more has a good chance to survive in a modern hospital, and some even smaller make the grade. And since many conditions calling for induction of premature labor in the last trimester—such as toxemia (blood poisoning) or eclampsia (convulsive seizures), placenta previa (abnormal position of the placenta, closing the mouth of the uterus), advanced and intractable (unmanageable) diabetes, and a few others—threaten the life of the baby as well as that of the mother, the operation can well be considered to be in the interest of both mother and child.

Among the many indications or reasons for performing therapeutic abortions given in textbooks of fifty years or more ago the chief one was a severely contracted pelvis. This has long since been abandoned as a Caesarean section at or near term is a much safer procedure than induced abortion at any period. Tuberculosis was perhaps the next reason for this procedure, but this is now considered only in advanced cases which do not improve with prolonged bed rest, chemotherapy, or selected antibiotics. As a rule, pregnant women tend to gain considerable weight, which is favorable to the tubercular, so that with the additional aids of bed rest and medical treatments the average case can be arrested. However, great care must be exercised to prevent a relapse after delivery, as well as to prevent the infection of the baby, which cannot be nursed and should even not be exposed to its mother if the disease is active.

Though comparatively rare, there are many other conditions that may call for a therapeutic abortion. As this is not a medical treatise, I shall attempt only to mention some of them, with the observation that any condition which threatens the life or permanent health of the mother, or the life of the baby, should be considered. Among the conditions that deserve special mention is recurrent erythroblastosis (a blood disease of the newborn baby). Still, this is controversial, since most of these cases can be prevented or cured by early recognition and prompt and energetic treatment, immediately after birth. Every expectant mother with a negative Rh factor whose husband is Rh positive is a potential source of an erythroblastotic baby. Such a mother should practice rigid contraception, and, if pregnancy does occur, should be carefully watched by the obstetrician with pediatric consultation. After the loss of one or more babies from this condition in spite of efficient treatment, she should have the benefit of obstetric and pediatric consultation, looking to the advisability of a therapeutic abortion.

Tumors, external to the birth canal, such as fibroid, ovarian tumors, and others, formerly considered reasons for induced abortions, are now successfully treated by surgery. Tumors within the birth canal are generally valid reasons for inducing an abortion, as they will in most cases eventually produce abortion anyway. This applies particularly to hydatid mole (a degenerating mass formed in the uterus), polyhydramnion (excessive amount of fluid in the fetal membranes), and fetal death from any cause. Any severe and prolonged uterine bleeding should be similarly taken care of, as it will eventually cause an abortion and may cause an irreversible blood loss. Patients who bleed severely should have their hemoglobin checked frequently.

Cancer during pregnancy is a very serious matter and unless treated heroically (boldly) may cause the death of both mother and child. If this condition, within the uterus or cervix, is found early and in an operable or curable stage, surgery should be resorted to regardless of the pregnancy. If, however, it has progressed to an incurable stage, as is frequently the case before recognition, the pregnancy may be allowed to progress, as it will not seriously accelerate the cancer and may give the mother the supreme happiness of having her baby in her last days.

One of the commonest indications for an abortion, though at the present time not nearly so common as formerly, is *pernicious* vomiting of pregnancy, i.e., the true or toxic type. The physician must distinguish between the true or toxic type and that induced by a psychological aversion to, or fear of, pregnancy. This latter condition may be successfully handled by psychiatric treatment. But if hospital studies reveal toxic vomiting, which is not relieved by rest, sedation, intravenous treatment, or other means, then we have a real need for therapeutic abortion, because this type of vomiting may threaten life itself.

But let no pregnant mothers become unduly alarmed! These cases, fortunately, occur but seldom. Yet they mean a real problem when they do occur, a problem that must be faced courageously. In my opinion a physician is cowardly who does not face this condition with courage and determination to save the mother's life. Nor can he escape his responsibility by leaving the case "in God's hands." Naturally a physician should ask for God's guidance in this kind of situation, as he should in all serious cases, and even in all his routine practice. I feel, however, that God has placed physicians here for the definite purpose of service to humanity, and as an agent between Him and the patient. With professional training and God-given intelligence we are not justified in leaving things of this sort to God's care alone; not, at least, until we have exhausted every possible known method of treatment. This matter needs some stress. Not all physicians act bravely when they should. It stands to reason, of course, that the physician should always ask for consultation, and that he *must* have it before he takes any radical step.

Serious organic heart disease is also a condition demanding serious consideration in pregnancy. The physician must consider the increasing strain of a progressing pregnancy, and particularly the strain of labor and delivery. In all such cases careful cardiac study and consultation are called for. I think that it is generally agreed that if the heart muscle is definitely weakened a therapeutic abortion is justified.

Nephritis, or Bright's disease, if severe, is another indication for an abortion. This also applies to hypertension with serious kidney involvement of any sort. However, we now have a much better therapeutic armamentarium for treating these cases than formerly, and with a urologist's help many such cases can be treated successfully and the pregnancy can be allowed to proceed. For instance, in stricture of the ureter, or so-called blocked kidney, the urologist can pass a catheter right up to the kidney and drain it. This procedure, together with our present powerful urinary antiseptics or antibiotics, will combat practically all local kidney infections. The physician, however, must guard against leaving the kidneys so damaged that, even though the baby is saved, the involvement will progress until it takes the life of the mother, sooner or later, after the birth of the baby.

There are many other conditions which occasionally demand a therapeutic abortion, but they hardly need be enumerated here. Let it be sufficient to say that any condition that threatens the life of the mother, either immediately or in the foreseeable future, should be deemed a sufficient reason for the interruption of pregnancy. The Christian physician will always be alert for such situations, and when he comes upon one will do his utmost in medical study and action, and at the same time will "take it to the Lord in prayer." He will seek the best in hospitalization and consultation, and will avoid those physicians whose religious scruples nearly always revolve around the thought of saving the baby only. If the mother is saved, there may be other babies later; if she is lost, very often all is lost. For in placing the interests of the mother second to those of the baby there is every possibility of the mother's inert body becoming the coffin of the baby.

PART III

STERILIZATION

11

LATEST DEVELOPMENTS IN THE
PRACTICE OF STERILIZATION

Daniel G. Morton

Dr. Morton, an **Episcopalian,** is Professor of Obstetrics and Gynecology at the University of California School of Medicine in Los Angeles, California.

Human sterilization may be defined as any treatment or operative procedure that destroys the procreative ability of man. An element of permanency is implied in this definition and therefore it does not include contraceptive measures that render a person sterile for a temporary period only.

Sterilization may apply to either the male or the female. Actually many operative procedures upon the genitalia of men and women may effect sterilization though the intent of the operation may be directed primarily to eradicating disease rather than to sterilization per se. Strictly speaking the term sterilization is confined to procedures carried out solely for the purpose of destroying the reproductive capacity and is not employed when referring to procedures carried out primarily for other reasons.

Since sterilization interferes with procreation it is closely allied to induced abortion in the minds of many people. Actually there is no similarity between the two: induced abortion destroys life in its incipiency, while sterilization prevents it from occurring and in this sense is no different from *any* measure of avoidance, including simple abstinence.

Sterilization is prohibited by the Roman Catholic Church, for whatever reason, except that which is incident to the removal of the genital organs for a medical indication. While Protestants and those of other religions, so far as I am aware, do not have specific prohibitions against sterilization, there remains a great body of public and religious opinion that there is something immoral about it. The reasons for this are not clear, but it seems very likely that an important element contributing to this viewpoint is a repugnance in human beings against anything which deprives a person of his natural rights and privileges. And about sterilization there does indeed hang an aura of the involuntary, of a deed imposed rather than welcomed or even sought. Because of this general opinion and regardless of the reasons for it, sterilizations have not been performed freely and merely for the bidding. Most hospital staffs in the United States require consultation and a medical indication for the performance of a sterilization procedure.

In recent years, perhaps the last ten or even twenty years as my personal experience indicates, public opinion has been shifting and many individuals have branded the point of view just expressed as irrational, and they have adopted a much more liberal attitude. In some nations today (notably India and Japan) there even exist programs of voluntary sterilization supported by public funds for the purpose of population control. Indeed, there is a rapidly growing body of opinion that the operation should be available for the asking, provided both husband and wife understand and appreciate the implications and risks of the procedure, which incidentally are few in number. However, we should repeat that this is not the predominant point of view today, even though it is a rapidly growing one.

In some forty-five states there is no law relating to sterilization outside of psychiatric institutions. The operation is specifically prohibited by law in the four states of Connecticut, Kansas, Montana, and Utah. In 1962 Virginia enacted a law authorizing physicians to perform sexual-sterilization operations on persons twenty-one years of age or older who request it. This is the only state so far to enact such a law. However, there are twenty-nine states that have laws expressly authorizing eugenic sterilization. In this connection various mechanisms have been established to determine the desirability of such operations and at the same time afford protection against unwarranted procedures.

While only the four states mentioned have laws specifically prohibiting sterilization, because of the moral considerations mentioned, the legal status of one performing this operation, except on medical indication, is somewhat precarious. Such an individual is open to the charge of committing mayhem upon the person of his patient. Other possibilities of dissatisfaction, and thus legal action, are failure of the operation to effect sterilization, the development of subsequent impotence, or a situation leading to the desire for more children. For these reasons the legal departments of the American Medical Association and of most County Medical Associations advise against sterilization procedures for other than medical indications.

Nevertheless it is well known that these operations are being performed widely when both husband and wife desire it and are willing to sign a written statement of their desire, in spite of the possible legal hazard incurred by the operator. Many legal authorities hold that under these circumstances the risk is slight. Usually such operations are performed upon the male because the operation of vasectomy, which destroys the continuity of the *vas deferens* (seed-carrying duct), is a simple one and indeed is often performed under local anesthesia as an office procedure. In the female a sterilizing operation is much more complicated since ligation and interruption of continuity of the oviducts (or Fallopian tubes) requires opening of the abdomen.

The methods of effecting sterilization are several: (1) by castration, which may be brought about by exposure of the gonads (sexual glands) to ionizing radiation such as X-rays, radium, or radioactive cobalt, etc., or it may be accomplished by surgical removal of the gonads; (2) by interference with the opportunity for the sperm and egg to come together, which may be effected surgically by removal or ligation of the male tubes on each side (the *vas deferens*), or of the oviducts (Fallopian tubes) in the female; (3) by performing a hysterectomy in the female, i.e., removal of the uterus. Another method of sterilizing the female which has been tried with only moderate success is cauterization (burning or searing) of the openings of the oviducts into the uterine cavity by inserting a cautery tip up through the cervix and uterus to the desired sites. This is a blind procedure and has not been successful enough to consider further. Its chief virtue is avoidance of the necessity for opening the abdomen.

Sterilization of males by castration was practiced in ancient times, the purpose having been not only to prevent reproduction but also to destroy the ability to have sexual intercourse. If the castration was carried out before puberty an individual was produced who could safely be used as a harem attendant. Such persons were referred to as eunuchs. Castration does indeed render the male sterile in all instances, though it does not always render him incapable of sexual intercourse unless performed before puberty. Just as women who have been castrated (removal of oviducts or uterus) may continue to have libido and satisfactory sexual response, so may the male fare likewise.

Castration has been employed to sterilize and to destroy sexual interest in more modern times in individuals who were sexual psychopaths, or who exhibited an unmanageable sexual perversion. In 1929 Whitney reported the castration of thirteen individuals of this type ranging in age from thirteen to thirty-nine years, with completely beneficial results.

The most common operation for the production of sterility in the male is called *vasectomy* because it has to do with the destruction of the continuity of the *vas deferens*, a small somewhat less than pencil-sized tube that conducts the sperm from the testicle up through the scrotum and inguinal canal to the seminal vesicles at the base of the bladder where they are stored until ejaculation occurs. The *vas deferens* can be approached surgically very easily as it traverses the upper half of the scrotum. It can be palpated (touched or felt) in this area and approached through a small skin incision. Usually a short segment is removed and the remaining free ends are ligated securely. There are of course two such tubes, one from each testicle. The operation is a minor one and is often performed under local anesthesia. It is highly successful, though failures have been reported on rare occasions, presumably due to the re-establishment by nature of a tubular connection between the two cut ends. Ordinarily there are no ill effects either immediate or remote. The operation does not interfere in any way with the normal physiology of the sex organs. Adverse effects upon sexual potency have been reported occasionally; invariably they have been due to misinformation on the part of the patient. Should the belief exist that the operation will produce impotence, then the possibility of its development is present. Such an effect would be psychological rather than physical—a vivid example of the very real interrelatedness of the psyche and the physical body.

Re-establishment of the continuity of these ducts has often been accomplished. Generally the male who has sought sterilization does not change his mind at a later time, but occasionally circumstances do arise which make re-establishment of fertility desirable. The operation to re-establish continuity is not always successful, however, even in the most expert surgeon's hands.

In the female a sterilizing operation is more complicated than in the male. Ligation and interruption of continuity of the oviducts (or Fallopian tubes) requires opening of the abdomen, or a difficult approach through the vagina, between the bladder and the uterus. In any event, a period of hospitalization is required. These operations in women are usually not performed as the sole procedure. Quite frequently the tubal sterilization is performed at the same time as some other operation demanding the opening of the abdomen, e.g., Caesarean section. There are a number of different techniques of tubal sterilization some of which have been more successful than others. The details are not appropriate to this discussion.

In 1953 Thomas reviewed 35,000 tubal sterilization operations of all types and found a failure rate of one in 200. The best method probably fails no more frequently than once in 300. A few deaths have followed sterilization operations, usually because of some complication unassociated with the risk of the specific operation.

Re-establishment of the continuity of the oviducts has been reported. In some instances the ligated distal portions of the tubes have been successfully re-implanted into the uterine cavity. The success rate of such operations is low, however—perhaps one in five or more.

Hysterectomy has been employed for the purpose of sterilization more and more frequently in recent years. This seems like a rather drastic method of accomplishing sterilization, but actually the risk is little if any greater than for the tubal operations when adequate thought is given to the proper selection of suitable candidates. Hysterectomy, as a means of sterilization, is almost never performed except in association with other operative procedures, e.g., at the time of a fourth or fifth Caesarean section, when the abdomen has to be opened anyway. In women who are nearing the end of their menstrual lives, say thirty-seven to forty-five years of age, removal of the uterus might well have a prophylactic value against cancer or other tumors as well as be an efficient method of sterilization. There is no turning back after this method of sterilization, however!

The reasons for sterilization might conveniently be divided into four major categories:

1. For medical indications—voluntary—on medical advice.

2. Statutory (on eugenic grounds), to prevent the reproduction of mental defectives and those with hereditary degenerative diseases.

3. Voluntary, according to the desires of the individual.

4. As a method of population control.

Sterilization for medical indication applies exclusively to women and is widely accepted in this country today, particularly if advised by one or more medical consultants. The general rule is to the effect that sterilization is indicated if in the opinion of the patient's physician and his consultants another pregnancy would seriously jeopardize the individual's future health. Usually previous failure of contraceptive measures is also a part of the argument for sterilization. Not infrequently the question arises when the patient is already pregnant and the decision to be made is whether therapeutic abortion and sterilization are indicated to save the life of the patient and to prevent further jeopardy.

The chief medical indications are irreversible chronic diseases that seriously hamper the ability to carry on a normal existence, such as severe heart disease, chronic kidney disease, pulmonary tuberculosis, debilitating neurological diseases, severe epilepsy, certain types of anemia, and some psychiatric conditions. Actually it has been shown that women with any of these diseases can frequently negotiate a pregnancy successfully and without serious harm, so that the tendency is toward very careful evaluation indeed before deciding that the disease is so incapacitating that further pregnancies are contraindicated.

Rather frequently other considerations enter in, such as the woman's age, the number of children she already has, and the home conditions. For example, a twenty-four-year-old woman with recently arrested pulmonary tuberculosis, with-

out children, with excellent home conditions, an adequate
financial income, and a capable, understanding husband,
might well have a baby without serious hazard to her health,
whereas it would be foolish and dangerous for a forty-year-
old with five children, a drunken husband, and little or no
financial stability, to have a sixth child.

Psychiatric indications are especially difficult to evaluate
and expert consultation is absolutely essential. At best it is
often impossible to prognosticate the outcome in the case of
many psychotic patients.

One of the most controversial indications today is "grand
multiparity," ordinarily defined as the state of having had six
children. At one time it was shown by Dr. Nicholson Eastman
of the Johns Hopkins Hospital that the risk of complications
and maternal death increased progressively as the number of
pregnancies increased after six. This led to the practice of
offering sterilization to women in these categories. Indeed,
many doctors extended this principle and offered sterilization to women in the immediate postpartum period (directly
after childbirth) who had had four or even three babies, particularly if at this time they were somewhat older. Various
combinations of age and parity (number of children) were
employed and still are. However, Dr. Eastman found that the
sterilization operations were not without danger and several
patients died, sufficient in number to exceed the risk of greater
multiparity. Following this latter experience a more conservative attitude developed with respect to grand multiparity as a
medical indication for postpartum sterilization. Actually the
risk is slight indeed if all proper precautions are observed.
It has been learned, for example, that more risk is incurred
if the operation is done in the postpartum period than if it is
done some months later, due to a greater danger of infection
at this time. On the other hand, if it is to be done in the
postpartum period it is safest to do it early, i.e., within twenty-
four hours after delivery.

Sterilization is considered indicated in most instances at

the time of a third Caesarean section. This rule of thumb came to prevail a good many years ago when the risk of Caesarean section was much greater than it is today, both because of infection and in a subsequent pregnancy because of a defective scar that might rupture and cause the death of the baby and sometimes of the mother. It was considered unsafe to allow a woman to have a fourth pregnancy. But nowadays infections are rare, and a different type of incision is made in the uterus which results in a much safer scar. Ruptures still do occur on rare occasions, however. It has been learned that women may have almost any number of children they desire in spite of requiring repeated Caesarean sections, provided there is good healing each time and the condition of the uterine wall remains good. Some women have had eight and ten Caesarean sections without incident. However, most obstetricians are still willing to perform sterilization at the third Caesarean section if the patient so desires. Exceptions might be in those who are very young and whose lot in life might change. On the other hand, some obstetricians feel that sterilization is justified at the second Caesarean section in women who are in their late thirties or early forties and who so desire.

Sterilizations of the statutory type (on eugenic grounds) were performed rather frequently some twenty years ago but are employed less often at the present time. This decreasing frequency has not been due to operative complications, or to operative mortality (although there have been a few deaths reported, as is the case in any and all operative procedures). Rather, there seems to be some lessening of the conviction that sterilization makes a significant contribution to the prevention of mental defectives. It is difficult to judge how sound this change of belief is. It is quite certain that when defective breeds with defective (except for those of environmental origin) the results are tragic in terms of the propagation of more defectives. Nevertheless an increasing repugnance against depriving even those of seriously defective caliber of their procreative abilities has found its way into modern thinking. Perhaps this is a proper attitude. Certainly, it has been learned that many, perhaps the majority, of the cases of defective central-nervous-system development are due to environmental factors only and are clearly without hereditary implications.

Voluntary sterilization, upon request of an individual for personal, perhaps completely nonmedical reasons, has not yet achieved either general or religious acceptance. As indicated above, however, such sterilizations are performed rather widely, almost always upon the male. And who is there to say that this is wrong? It is to be expected that the practice will grow as a matter of convenience—as a practical and convenient method of birth control. In essence it does not differ from other methods of control, such as abstinence, or rhythm control, or the use of contraceptive measures. It is simply more certain and more permanent.

Some few male sterilizations are performed for a *medical* reason—to avoid additional pregnancies in the wife, because it is an easier operation to perform and has fewer complications than sterilization of the female. This is probably rarely indicated. It is generally agreed that the male should not be sterilized for the sake of his spouse unless there is some urgent reason, or they both desire it unequivocally.

As a method of population control it seems unlikely that sterilization could or should occupy a very important place. It is being used in India and some other countries for population control. However, it could never be applied widely enough to cause any appreciable drop in the birth rate and must be regarded as a supplementary method of birth control only.

As indicated above, the success rate for sterilization operations is very high in both the male and the female. Probably not more than three or four out of 1,000 cases fail. The failures are remarkable examples of nature's ability to establish a new channel between the ligated ends of the severed tubes.

Unfavorable psychological reactions occasionally occur, with relative or absolute impotence on the part of the male and inability to arrive at an orgasm in women. These unhappy events take place only when ignorance prevails. Should the male patient believe that the operation will result in loss of potency, and the female patient that she will lose the ability to have an orgasm (and many do so unless informed to the contrary) the belief is likely to turn into reality. It is the physician's obligation to make sure that the candidate for sterilization is fully informed.

Operative complications are few, though it must be appreciated that *any* operation, no matter how slight, entails some risk, either from the procedure itself or from the anesthetic. Infection may result, particularly if the operation is done at certain periods in the puerperium (the state of a woman soon after childbirth) or in the presence of known genital infection. It can usually be avoided by careful selection of time and proper preparation of the patient. As stated, a few deaths have occurred. Generally speaking, however, the risk is no greater than most of us take driving an automobile every day on the busy streets of any American city.

12

A USEFUL PROCEDURE OF PREVENTIVE MEDICINE

Owen Jones Toland

Dr. Toland is Chief Obstetrician and Gynecologist at the Episcopal Hospital in Philadelphia. He is a member of the **Episcopal Church.**

As most of my readers know, sterilization is a procedure that has its origins in antiquity. Males have been castrated in the Orient, particularly in Egypt, Babylonia, and Persia, since the earliest times, mostly for social reasons (eunuchism). Ancient Israel often followed the example of the larger nations. The Bible tells us that castrated individuals were employed at King David's court (I Chron. 28:1) and at the courts of several of the later kings of Judah and the Northern Kingdom (II Kings 24:15; 25:19; Jer. 29:2, etc.). In most instances the Bible in its translations refers to these castrates as "officers." Some Bible scholars believe that these "officers" among Israel were not Jews but foreigners.

What is perhaps not so well known is that castration or sterilization was also frequently practiced among the early Christians. Soon after the time of the Apostles a variety of sects appeared among the early Christians, and some of these sects had the notion that anything "fleshly" and sexual in human life was tainted with sin. These beliefs spread, and before long groups of Christian devotees had themselves castrated as a method of avoiding sexual sin, thus better to insure salvation for themselves. In the days of St. Augustine one of those sects had reached considerable proportions. They were known as the Valesii, and St. Augustine says of them, "The Valesii castrate themselves . . . thinking thereby to serve God."

Nor was self-mutilation for the enhancement of the spiritual life confined to those early times. Practically all through the Christian era there have been sects and extremist groups among Christian believers that were obsessed with extravagant and esoteric notions, and frequently they sought to "crucify the flesh" in a very realistic way by castration. Even during the nineteenth century a sect appeared in Czarist Russia known as the Skoptsi that grew to such proportions that the Russian authorities decided to deport many of them to Siberia in order to break up the cult and put a stop to castrations for religious purposes. In 1874 this cult was still estimated to have something like five thousand adherents.

In view of these facts it seems odd that today the Roman Catholic Church, the chief opponent of sterilization on moral grounds, regards the medical sterilization act as one of "mortal sin." This belief, however, did not prevent the castrating of Italian boys over a protracted period in order to insure their quality and durability as soprano singers in church choirs. In 1878 Pope Leo XIII happily put an end to this practice, for all time.

But let us proceed. Since the dawn of human experience it has been universally recognized that the sexual urge is one of the most explosive forces inherent in humanity. Primitive people were—and are—thoroughly aware of this, and they saturated sex with taboos and cluttered it with rituals. Their so-called civilized successors have in their own more sophisticated style accomplished remarkably parallel results.

It was not until comparatively modern times that the results of the sex urge were regarded at all objectively. Early in the nineteenth century Thomas R. Malthus, an English clergyman-economist, recognized that a relationship existed between population growth and the trilogy of war, famine, and disease. But in his program for ameliorating conditions he had no other practicable measures to recommend than the one of "moral restraint." Yet his continued efforts to enlist supporters did start people thinking about the subject. It was a slow process, however, and more than a hundred years elapsed before any more effective practical means were at hand besides the practice of self-control to restrict human fecundity. I should mention that a French clinician named Condom, many years earlier, had invented a device that still bears his name for the control of the spread of venereal disease. Refinements of this "preventive" gradually came to be used by male partners for the purpose of family limitation as well. Today they are retailed by the millions in this country and elsewhere.

The real impetus to stem the tide of procreation had to wait for Margaret Sanger. Early in this century she pointed out with precise accuracy and undeniable logic that a most intimate relationship exists between poverty and all its attendant misery and unrestricted human spawning. It seems odd that so very obvious a deduction should have escaped articulate human attention for so long, but such is the fact. Margaret Sanger's crusade for "birth control" carries on today under the more decorous title of "planned parenthood." Unquestionably some of Mrs. Sanger's success sprang from the invention of the occlusive vaginal diaphragm and its importation into this country. This device for the first time placed an effective mechanism for avoiding conception into the hands of the female partner, without greatly upsetting the harmony of sexual intercourse.

In its earlier phases the "birth control" movement was to those who carried the torch a bona fide crusade. The fervor aroused among its devotees was something like the emotional intensity of the campaign for "votes for women." But the test of time has shown that the results accruing from the Margaret Sanger crusade hardly fulfill the initial hopes of its votaries. In this connection let it be remembered that many of the advocates of female suffrage sincerely believed that practically all social evil would be automatically eliminated by its enactment into law. The present American scene speaks for itself.

Yet, "planned parenthood" has now become an almost universally accepted practice in this country, whether admitted or not. It is very much a part of "the American way of life." I can testify from prolonged clinical experience and acquaintance with the intimate affairs of many families that its acceptance has immeasurably benefited unnumbered American marriages. This surely is no mean accomplishment. And I doubt exceedingly that it has promoted the spread of immorality. I doubt that "planned parenthood" fostered immorality any more than female suffrage eliminated it.

The principal reason for the long delay in achieving anything approaching mass distribution of the diaphragm method of contraception was that the co-operation of the medical profession was essential. The profession is properly conservative and does not lightly alter its established patterns of thinking. This is particularly the case when the impetus for change initiates from lay sources, as in the "birth control" movement. Furthermore, prolonged professional experience with the diaphragm method of conception control showed that it was subject to considerable limitations. It did not prove to be the all-efficient panacea originally hoped for by its advocates.

All this leads to the subject of sterilization as it is practiced today. Those actively engaged in the business of ushering new life into the world have learned that contraceptive techniques are but a partial answer to the existing requirements of voluntary family limitation. Religious considerations bar their use for a large group, and for a far larger group their employment is impracticable by reason of what might be termed "emotional immaturity." The latter group is almost limitless, and, naturally enough, its members are the individuals that most urgently require protection from the results of their natural urges. It is here that permanent sterilization by surgical means finds its largest field of application. Thanks to the advances of modern surgery, the risk attendant upon surgical sterilizations is practically negligible. The usual convenient time for its performance is shortly postpartum (after childbirth). The surgical details of sterilization, both in the male and the female, have been dealt with in a previous chapter, so there is no use going into unnecessary duplication. Inasmuch as it is the woman who bears the burden of pregnancy and delivery, and the far heavier one of raising the children, the indication for a sterilization operation occurs continually in obstetric practice. The operation impairs none of the regular functions—ovulation, menstruation, or sex response. It has been my experience that the last mentioned is often greatly enhanced by banishing the fear of unwanted pregnancy.

About twenty years ago the late Dr. Frederick L. Adair of Chicago (at that time called the "Dean of American Obstetrics") had the courage to recommend that multiparity (the condition of having borne several children) in and by itself was sufficient indication for the performance of sterilization. He backed his opinion with a series of illustrative cases, where the operation was performed shortly after confinement. A second series shortly thereafter appeared from the department of obstetrics of the University of Virginia Medical School. These presentations were a lead badly needed by the medical profession, which for years had considered the operation taboo, even disreputable, unless there were "medical indications." Dr. Adair's enormous prestige and the University of Virginia's high reputation provided a shield of respectability most welcome in gaining the cooperation of other leaders in our specialty. Today the apprentice physician is oriented toward the concept of adding this operation to his therapeutic armamentarium in most non-Catholic medical schools, and the procedure has become com-

monly accepted practice in many hospitals, subject of course
to certain regulations.

Perhaps I might venture a word as to my opinion of the
physician's responsibility to the patient in this matter. I feel
that, first and foremost, one should be alert to recognize that
such an operation might be life saving. Next to this, I feel
that one should avoid having any fixed and sharply defined
rules: each case should be considered individually. I am confident that any physician of average intelligence and good will
will make remarkably few errors if he feels intrinsically that
the procedure is warranted for a particular patient, from the
point of view of her long-range welfare. The patient may have
no children, or many, or anywhere in between. There will be
many times when the suggestion will be made by the patient,
and the physician will then do his best to soft-pedal it or refuse to co-operate. I have found this approach useful. If one
is honestly in doubt as to the desirability of a sterilizing operation, it should be postponed for at least six months. In this
way errors can easily be avoided, and it puts the responsibility where it belongs—back on the patient. I have noticed
that patients so deferred rarely return for the procedure.

I can recall only one instance, in an experience of one-
third of a century, when a patient regretted the operation.
She had had nine children by the time she was twenty-eight
years old. She just loved babies! When this is compared with
the satisfaction of seeing the burden of living rendered more
tolerable in a great number of lives, the chagrin of one bad
result seems a very small price to pay. I know of no operation
where the enduring gratitude of patients is so out of propor-
tion to the actual service rendered. To mention only one
facet: the woman who consults you in desperation because
of a pregnancy that to her is a catastrophic situation and
pleads for an abortion—such a woman usually finds a fair
degree of serenity when assured that if she has this baby, the
situation will never rise again.

My thirty-five years of experience as a practicing obstetrician only inclines me to be ever more strongly in favor of a wider recognition of therapeutic sterilization as a useful procedure of preventive medicine. I think this term is justified when one considers the underlying motive and its results. I can assure the reader that it holds, when wisely utilized, great potentialities for making a healthier, happier family life.

As to objections of a religious nature, I am unable to see or grant their validity. The procedure as I have briefly described it is in my opinion ethical, and it is advantageous to the physical and social welfare of the right kind of patient, and hence in agreement with religious precepts.

13

A CLOSE LOOK AT THE RESULTS OF SEXUAL STERILIZATION

JOHN C. BROUGHER

> **Dr. Brougher** is a Specialist in Gynecology and Obstetrics at the Vancouver Clinic in Vancouver, Washington. He is a **Protestant.**

Back in 1779 Johann Peter Frank, a German physician and philosopher, urged that both the mentally diseased and the mentally deficient be castrated to prevent the deterioration of the race.[1] (*Castration* usually means to deprive one of reproductive ability by removal of the testicles, in the male, or of the ovaries, in the female. *Sterilization,* in modern times, usually means achieving the same end by less radical surgical means.) In 1897, more than a century after Dr. Frank's effort, a bill providing for eugenic sterilization was introduced in the Michigan legislature but failed of passage. Two years later Dr. Harry Sharp began systematic sterilization at the Indiana State Reformatory by the method of vasectomy (operation on the inner seed-conveying ducts), which had none of the disadvantages of castration.[2]

In 1905 the legislature of the Commonwealth of Pennsylvania passed the first institutional sterilization law, but it was vetoed by the governor. But two years after that the State of

[1] E. S. Gosney, and Paul Popenoe, *Sterilization for Human Betterment,* The Macmillan Co., New York, 1929.
[2] See footnote 1.

Indiana adopted such a law, and again two years later, in 1909, Washington and California followed. Presently, twenty-eight of the states have this law on their statute books.[3] There are twenty states that have no laws pertaining to sterilization, while four states, Connecticut, Kansas, Montana, and Utah, not only have laws pertaining to institutional sterilization but also those which provide that no sterilization may be performed outside of institutions except for "medical necessity."[4] On March 5, 1942, the Supreme Court of the State of Washington found the sterilization act unconstitutional, thus prohibiting institutional sterilization in that state.[5] At the writing of this chapter, in 1962, Virginia took a step of historic significance. The General Assembly of that state passed a bill explicitly legalizing voluntary sterilization. It became the first state to sanction the operation for other than therapeutic or genetic reasons, simply at the request of the adult individuals concerned, the attending physicians agreeing. The new law, of course, makes certain necessary stipulations.

In January, 1955, Craig reported that a total of 57,218 official eugenic sterilizations had been performed in the twenty-eight states. The indications were as follows: mental illness, 44 per cent; mental deficiency, 51 per cent; epilepsy and less-common indications, 5 per cent. He observed that the annual number of eugenic sterilizations had decreased from *circa* 3,000 a year in the 1930s to 1,100 in 1957. This, he stated, was partly due to a growing uncertainty as to the respective influence of heredity and environment in the genesis of certain types of mental disorder. Oregon, as a single example of the incidence of sterilization, had thirty-nine cases

[3] Roy Dale Craig, *American Journal of Obstetrics and Gynecology*, Vol. 74, No. 2, 328, August, 1957.
[4] Ruth P. Smith, Executive Director, Human Betterment Association of America, Inc. Personal communication, with permission, January 4, 1962.
[5] Van R. Hinkle, Department of Institutions, Olympia, Wash. Personal communication, with permission, December 1, 1961.

for patients in Oregon State Hospital from January 1, 1956, to November 30, 1961.[6]

In those states where sterilization is legal the medical indications are governed by laws that make it possible to sterilize certain types of criminal or mental patients. The object is to prevent the birth of children who may have criminal sexual psychopathy, heredofamilial degenerative diseases (hereditary in a family), or who may suffer from certain types of mental disease, including feeble-mindedness. "Statutory or eugenic sterilization" is done only in state or mental hospitals. The rapid increase in the number of inmates of institutions and the cost of their care should be sufficient argument for eugenic control.

Popenoe, in 1929, reported on the sterilization of 6,225 patients in psychiatric hospitals with no untoward results. Rather, he states, "after their release, in case after case, the operation was the only thing that enabled the family to be kept together and the patient to remain in the community instead of returning to the state hospital."[7]

The words "sexual sterilization" used in relation to modern medical ethics and practice refer either to a voluntary request by the individual or to a recommendation by the physician for the performance of a procedure which has the intended result of producing inability to procreate. Physicians use the term "therapeutic sterilization" only when conditions present make this type of surgery life saving to the mother. These conditions, or medical indications, include chronic hypertensive states (high blood pressure), rheumatic heart disease in advanced form, pulmonary tuberculosis, advanced kidney disease, and certain mental diseases that are considered inheritable. Certain physical defects such as blindness, deafness, or crippling deformities may also constitute medical reasons

[6] Richard H. Wilcox, Oregon State Board of Eugenics, Portland, Ore. Personal communication, with permission, November 30, 1961.
[7] Paul Popenoe, *New England Journal of Medicine,* 201:880, 1929.

for sterilization. A third type known as "socio-economic sterilization" is relatively modern. This type of sterilization is practiced rather widely these days in families whose financial condition would hardly permit another pregnancy or the cost of rearing another child. The operation is frequently performed on the man, in the privacy of a doctor's office, and is a comparatively simple procedure.

In 1929 Gosney and Popenoe, in reviewing the histories of 420 normal women and sixty-five men who had been sterilized in private practice, found no adverse physical effects in either sex. For approximately one-third of these patients sexual life was improved. (See footnote 1)

Lam reported, in 1936, that 300 men in Honolulu, Hawaii, had vasectomies performed during the years 1930–36 as part of a birth control program. All these patients were on relief. They were considered average, normal men, and the operations were entirely voluntary. Of these patients 85 per cent were examined one year later, and then again four years after their surgery. No physical changes were noted in the testicles. Only two complained that their sexual potency had been impaired.[8]

In 1950 Garrison reported vasectomies on fifty mentally normal males in North Carolina. The motives were as follows: twenty-three had all the children they could care for, including one whose wife had borne him fourteen; the wives of nineteen had physical disabilities such as kidney disease, diabetes, or toxemia of pregnancy; eight cases had physical handicaps in the husband such as rheumatism, blindness, deafness, diabetes, and asthma. Only three patients regretted having had the operation.[9]

The increased demand for this operation in the male rather than the female is often based entirely on socio-economic factors and is largely resorted to because of the inefficiency

[8] J. W. Lam, *Journal of Contraception*, 1:159, 1936.
[9] P. L. Garrison, and C. J. Gamble, *Journal of the American Medical Association*, 144:293, 1950.

of present methods of birth control. With newer methods being developed in the hormone field, there may be less demand for male sterilization. However, the expense of these new preparations could still make surgery preferable where the economic factor is of prime importance.

The details of sterilization surgery, both in men and in women, have been satisfactorily discussed and explained in a preceding chapter, and for that reason we shall move on at this point to the question how people feel toward sterilization; particularly how sterilized women have reacted to their experience. Adams, in 1957, sent a questionnaire to 263 women who had been sterilized.[10] The benefit of such studies is important in attaining a goal of standardization for such procedures in the hospital. It is desirable to perform this operation only in women who later will not have regrets.

Dr. Adams found, in compiling the results of the answers, that among the 173 who returned the questionnaire health was worse in only two patients. These two complained of heavier periods (which may not have been related to surgery at all) but were glad they had been sterilized. Sexual enjoyment had not changed in 47 per cent of these cases, it was increased in 49½ per cent, and had become worse in 3½ per cent. Of this small percentage it was found that all except one were glad that the operation had been done. One felt that finances were the main cause of her sexual problem. (It is of course well known that many psychic factors play a role in sexual response.) The mothers' attitude toward life had grown less favorable in only 1 per cent, and these two women admitted many other troubles, such as financial problems, lack of friends, and living in unfinished houses. Neither condemned the operation. The menstrual cycle showed, in the majority of the women, no changes. As regards discomfort, 80 4/10 per cent had noticed no change, 13 8/10 per cent

[10] Theodore W. Adams, *A Review of the Postpartum Sterilization Problem*, 1957. (Unpublished and used with permission.)

had more discomfort, and 5 8/10 per cent had less discomfort.

The questions of most interest were two that dealt with the patient's attitude toward sterilization. The answers: 88 5/10 per cent were glad the operation had been done, 2 9/10 per cent were sorry, and 8 6/10 per cent were indifferent. Upon the question whether they would like to be fertile again, the women's answer was interesting: only 6 3/10 per cent indicated they would. One question dealt with the husband's attitude toward his wife after her sterilization. That attitude showed no change in 72 4/10 per cent of the cases and improvement in 27 6/10 per cent.

In 1957 Guttmacher reported in his review of 544 women who had been sterilized after delivery that approximately one in twenty regretted having had the operation.[11] Many authors have written on the subject of the effects of sterilization, and both they and clinical experience have shown that the operation has no effect, physically, upon a woman. When a change in libido (sex response) does occur it is much more frequently an increase than a decrease.

It is true that multiparity (many children) presents a medical problem, since after the eighth child there is an increased maternal mortality rate; also, pregnancies, after the eighth, are associated with elevated stillbirth and infant death rates.[12] Guttmacher, Chief of Obstetrics and Gynecology in the Mount Sinai Hospital, New York City, in the matter of parity (number of children) reported their procedure to be as follows: "(1) All patients, whether private or service (charity), should be treated alike. (2) After signed permission by the couple, any patient irrespective of age may have puerperal (after-delivery) sterilization performed if the delivery gives her six or more living children; if between thirty and thirty-

---

[11] Alan F. Guttmacher, *Fertility and Sterility,* Vol. 8, No. 6, Nov.–Dec., 1957.

[12] Nicholson J. Eastman, *Williams' Obstetrics,* 10th ed., Appleton-Century-Crofts, Inc., New York, 1950.

five years of age, five or more living children; if over thirty-five, four or more living children. (3) Sterilization may be performed in the course of a gynecologic operation or Caesarean section, at the discretion of the operator. (4) All other cases of sterilization on a woman must first have the approval of the Chief of Obstetrics and Gynecology."[13]

"Consultation" is the name given to the act of two or more physicians conferring together about a medical problem. Such consultation is mandatory for each sterilizing procedure in a standard hospital, just as it is for a Caesarean section or a curettage (act of removing tissue from inside the uterus, such as placenta or cancer). The consultation report becomes a part of the hospital chart. Because sterilization has legal as well as moral implications, in a panel discussion at the meeting of the American College of Surgeons in San Francisco, in 1951, it was recommended a hospital medical board of seven physicians, representing the different specialities, be set up to receive and consider all requests for sterilization. Many hospitals have adopted such a plan or something like it. Roman Catholic hospitals do not approve of sterilization in either the male or the female, and it cannot be performed therein. Some hospitals permit it only when there is a medical reason, while a third category permit it for socio-economic as well as medical reasons. The Joint Commission on Accreditation of Hospitals insists that each hospital formulate rules and regulations for voluntary sterilization. They feel that this question is one that must be solved by the local hospital, dependent upon the feelings of the physicians as well as of the people of the community.[14] The American College of Obstetricians and Gynecologists makes the decision depend on individual

[13] Alan F. Guttmacher, *Scope Weekly*, reported by *World Wide Medical News Service*, April 2, 1958.
[14] Denver M. Vickers, Joint Commission on Accreditation of Hospitals. Personal communication, with permission, Nov. 16, 1961.

cases rather than on any set of rules which might be applied.[15]

As a legal protection, the physician must obtain proper consent from the husband and wife. The Human Betterment Association of America sent a questionnaire to 2,500 urologists and only ten instances of legal involvement were found. They investigated each of these and found no basis for the citation; therefore their statement holds true: "There is no case on record of a physician losing a suit brought against him for sterilization when proper consent had been obtained."[16] This association has a program of education, research, and direct aid in the field of voluntary sterilization, but help is given only to those who request it. This, as they term it, "is preventive social service since it attacks the cause by correcting a basic condition at the root of many instances of family distress."

What should be the physician's attitude toward sexual sterilization? A review of the medical literature on the subject reveals that physicians are attempting to standardize both the indications and the types of procedure. In this day of economic stress, when the standards of living have risen so high and the wants are so great, is it not imperative that, when possible, we control or limit the number of children in a family? To quote Dr. Robert L. Fawcett: "The housewife plays many roles—wife, companion, mother, sexual partner, homemaker, chauffeur, financier, teacher, and often auxiliary breadwinner."

This overworked and underpaid mother is deserving of every consideration from her family. The physician examines her and offers corrective measures. Sometimes it is medicine, but oftentimes it is reassurance and instruction that will en-

[15] Robert H. Kimbrough, The American College of Obstetricians and Gynecologists. Personal communication, with permission, Dec. 5, 1961.
[16] See footnote 3.

able her to meet and accept her problems. He may suggest family counseling by her minister, or he may suggest a psychiatrist. If fear of pregnancy plays a dominant role in her tension state, he may suggest birth control measures. She may request sterilization for herself or her husband. Should the doctor refuse, or should he grant her request? *Much in all this depends upon the individual's conscience.* [See Introduction, in the beginning of this volume. —EDITOR.]

Patients who, because of religious training, refrain from asking about birth control may have emotional conflicts because of an unsatisfactory sex life. There are Churches or sects who in their pronouncements have declared themselves against all forms of birth control, while other Churches allow so-called natural methods (rhythm) for family spacing or limitation. The physician must respect the loyalties or convictions of these patients and not bring about any feelings of conflict or guilt in suggesting other methods to them.

While this subject of sterilization may appear to be, at the present time, of only moderate importance to us as a nation, either socially or economically, nevertheless it must be admitted that overpopulation is a world problem, and it may become a national problem for us if our present trend of birth rate over death rate continues to climb. Burch in his article "Trends in the Incidence of Disease in the United States" says, "Mental illnesses are increasing in incidence in response to increase in population and the associated greater crowding, greater competition in the endeavors of life, and greater complexities of group and governmental activities."[17]

The United Nations Economic Council recognizes that living standards cannot be raised in many of the countries with low economic standards unless population growth can be restrained. Why shouldn't the United States, with the best medical care and the best-fed people in the world, lead the way to

[17] G. E. Burch, *World Medical Journal,* Vol. 8, No. 6:439, November, 1961.

better living standards, better families, better mental health, and happier homes?

The three indications for sterilization which have been considered are statutory or eugenic, medical or life saving, and socio-economic. The physician's role in this last indication is one of counselor. He does not suggest to the patient that he or she should be sterilized, but may grant the request if the indications are justifiable.

In this brief consideration of so great a medical, social, economic, eugenic, psychological, and religious problem as birth control by sexual sterilization, the author trusts that he has given the reader a basis for decision in this broadly social but also very personal question. In a free democratic country exchange of ideas is essential to progress. With the increase in life expectancy and the great decrease in the mortality rate of children during the past half-century, the problem of birth control has gained added significance. It is believed that adequate birth control, including sterilization in selected cases, may decrease the incidence of illegal abortion which is morally untenable as well as endangering to life.

Birth control by sterilization does not violate the principles of Christianity. Consider the following:

The love of man and woman for each other is essential to marital happiness, and the expression of devotion is not increased by a large family.

One of the basic needs of every human being is to feel that he is wanted.

It is immoral for parents to bring children into the world if their needs cannot be met: "But if any provide not for his own, and especially for those of his own house, he hath denied the faith, and is worse than an infidel." (I Tim. 5:8)

A child needs understanding, guidance, and Godly instruction, according to the Scriptural injunction, "Train up a child in the way he should go." (Prov. 22:6) Sometimes an overabundance of offspring makes the carrying out of that injunction an arduous task, if not an impossible one.

It should be the desire of both the physician and the parents to co-operate in producing wanted and well-adjusted individuals, who in turn must learn to live wisely and uprightly in our increasingly complex society.

14

THE ETHICS OF
STERILIZATION

Albert S. Bright

Dr. Bright, a **Protestant**, is a Specialist in Obstetrics and Gynecology in Bethesda, Maryland.

In present-day parlance "sterilization" means the obstruction of the pathway which allows human sperm and egg to meet.

It used to mean the removal of the sex glands—testes or gonads in men; ovaries in women. This was discontinued long ago, for it was determined that the sex glands in addition to creating the minute cells from which new life stems also had a vital influence on the health and well-being of the individual. The castrated male was not only sterile but his entire bodily function was altered. He became fat, lost his beard, and his voice changed. Often his efficiency for the tasks of life was greatly reduced. In the female profound changes were also made. She, too, became fat, developed facial hair, and a deep voice, and had severe hot flashes. These changes were produced by a lack of the male or female hormone, chemical substances produced by the testes or ovaries. Today these hormones are readily available in pill form and the undesirable changes described can be prevented.

Women usually escaped the old-fashioned castration because, fortunately, the ovaries are located inside the abdomen and thus were almost inaccessible until modern surgical techniques were developed. Dr. Ephraim MacDowell, a back-woods practitioner, was the first man in the United States to remove an ovary from a living woman for therapeutic purposes. He accomplished this operation in 1809, in a cabin in Kentucky, without benefit of anesthesia or antisepsis—and his patient outlived him by eleven years! This started things. For some time in the middle of the former century, under the influence of Dr. John Atlee of Philadelphia, removal of the ovaries became a medical fad. Today, however, they are removed only if they are seriously diseased or some other physical condition of the patient demands it.

The history of sterilization in the United States really began with the Eugenic Sterilization Laws. Eugenics is the study and cultivation of conditions that improve the physical and moral qualities of future generations. The term "eugenics" was coined by Sir Francis Dalton, a cousin of Charles Darwin. The rapid growth of the movement may be seen from the fact that in 1895 there were no laws in this country dealing with eugenics, while in 1937 there were eugenics laws on the books of thirty-two states. Three events at the end of the nineteenth century had hastened such interest: (1) Sir Francis Dalton's Eugenics Movement; (2) the rediscovery of Mendel's laws of heredity; (3) the development of safe, simple surgical techniques for sterilization.

In 1895 the superintendent of the State Home in Kansas began to sterilize mentally deficient inmates. This treatment became quite popular, and by 1921 about 3,900 persons had been rendered sterile, of which number about 80 per cent were mentally ill. In 1925 a famous decision was rendered by Justice Oliver Wendell Holmes of the United States Supreme Court in the case of Buck *vs*. Bell. Justice Holmes permitted the contested sterilization operation with the comment, "Three generations of imbeciles are enough." Sterilization does not violate the Fourteenth Amendment (which pertains to due process of law or equal protection under the law). At the present time twenty-six states have eugenic sterilization laws that are *compulsory*. In all of these states the mentally deficient are subject to the laws, and in all but two of them the law also applies to those with chronic mental illness.

Since in a foregoing chapter the techniques of sterilization have been discussed, and the conditions have been mentioned that must be met to have the operation take place, let us at this point proceed to examine the *ethics* of sterilization.

It is very difficult to assess the literature on this subject unless the religious views of the authors are taken into consideration. The published works of Roman Catholic writers are uniformly and completely antisterilization. A word about that presently.

A review of the historical record of the past hundred years or more reveals that the popularity of the operation has run in cycles: (1) From 1843 to 1880—a fad for oöphorectomy, or removal of both ovaries. At this time ovarian function was not understood. (2) From 1895 to 1930—a fad for eugenic sterilization. Again the exact hereditary effect of mental-defective-psychiatric diseases was not known. (3) From 1930 to 1955—a fad for sterilization because of medical diseases. Again more knowledge and better care have since shown that a large majority of the operations were not needed.

With the increase in man's knowledge these three fads have all but disappeared, and he finds that: (1) The ovaries are very important organs for the female and should never be removed unless they are seriously diseased. (2) The former ideas in regard to the need for sterilization of the feeble-minded and the insane have been greatly changed, so that now statutory or eugenic sterilization is rarely used. (3) Many medical conditions which formerly were believed to be fatal during pregnancy are no longer considered as such. Modern knowledge and therapy have rendered therapeutic sterilization no longer necessary in most cases of tuberculosis, heart disease, kidney disease, contracted (small) pelvis requiring Caesarean section for delivery, etc.

There are a few special medical conditions which sometimes do merit sterilization. For example:

1. The woman who has had many babies (over eight) and who hemorrhages following delivery.

2. Severe diabetes mellitus, especially when it has developed while the mother was young.

3. Severe fatal anemia of successive babies of a mother who has the Rh problem (adverse blood condition).

4. Hereditary deafness or blindness.

5. Inherited blood diseases such as hemophilia (poor coagulation and abnormal bleeding).

6. Severe rheumatoid arthritis.

7. Severe mental deficiency.

Now, what about sterilization for socio-economic reasons (voluntary sterilization)? This is by far the greatest question today. When is it proper to stop having children? Which is the right decision for parents? I am an obstetrician-gynecologist who has spent the last twenty-five years dealing with women, their problems and their diseases; and I have spent many hours in research study on this question. As a Christian man I have actually made it a subject of much prayer.

To quote a professor at one of our best-known medical schools: "To deny a healthy couple the privilege of parenthood of two or three healthy children simply on the basis of poverty would be unjustifiable, but to deny a couple the privilege of limiting their family when their economic burden is already more than they can bear comfortably is also unjustifiable." Pearl Buck has said, "In all those countries where population is too abundant the cause of the individual is lost."

There is much truth in that. In order to retain a healthy democracy, to keep true freedom, to prevent or remove one of the most potent causes of war, *the population must be limited.* And look at the problem from a different point of view. Remembering that man's chief aim should be to glorify God, we must surely reason that sickly and undernourished children, mentally or emotionally disturbed children, or parents chronically in debt certainly do not accomplish this end. An atmosphere of endless privation is hardly conducive to a spirit of thanksgiving and praise for blessings received.

In considering whether or not to request sterilization it should be remembered that modern surgery cannot put in a zipper that will allow the surgeon to do or undo the operation. It should also be remembered that even in the most expert hands not every operation, to the very last one, is successful. Occasionally pregnancies do occur after sterilization. But these are exceptions to the general rule.

The operation has no effect on the virility, sex life, or emotions of the person sterilized. He or she is the same after the operation as before; only there is no capability of reproduction. In men especially, there is a reticence about even considering the operation for fear of being changed in some way; and this attitude is easy to understand when one thinks of the stories handed down about eunuchs and the consequent improper understanding of the difference between sterilization and castration. However, because of the removal of a vital element out of one's existence, the admonition given by a certain obstetrician back in 1917 is still very pertinent today: "Sterilization, like marriage, should not be entered upon unadvisedly or lightly, but reverently, discreetly, advisedly, solemnly, and in the fear of God."

No discussion of the ethics of sterilization today can be complete without mentioning the absolute and dogmatic attitude toward this operation on the part of the Roman Catholic Church. After carefully studying many articles and the most recent available books on the ethics of sterilization by Catholic authors, let me present a summation of their ideas as fairly as I can.

Pope Pius XI has ruled, "Sterilization for the sole purpose of rendering a person incapable of parenthood is forbidden by the law of God, and hence may never be inflicted upon a man or a woman either by the individual's wish or against it, either by private or by public authority."[1]

Dr. J. R. Cavanagh states, "The natural law as interpreted by the Catholic Church says that human beings do not possess full dominion over themselves. That belongs to the Creator. Consequently a person has no right to mutilate his body unless this is needed to promote the welfare of the whole body."[2]

In his most recent definitive book on medical ethics C. A. McFadden, Ph.D., states that "the gift of life is bestowed upon us by the Author of all life and we thereby become custodians charged with its proper care."[3] (With this statement we heartily agree.) Dr. McFadden discusses sterilization from four points of view: (1) Socio-economic. This is absolutely contraindicated (forbidden) in Roman Catholic doctrine. (2) Therapeutic. Allowed only indirectly; for example, removal of the uterus for a tumor. (3) Eugenic (meaning that type of sterilization performed upon defective persons in the interest of social betterment). "It is a grave injustice to subject an innocent person to serious bodily mutilation merely for the sake of expediency or for the obtainment of objectives which can be procured just as effectively in a humane, decent, and moral manner." (4) Punitive. After much discussion by Dr. McFadden it appears that this is sometimes permitted, but usually forbidden.

[1] In his encyclical *Casti Connubii.*
[2] J. R. Cavanagh, *Fundamentals of Marriage Counseling,* Bruce Publishing Co., Milwaukee, 1960.
[3] C. A. McFadden, *Roman Catholic Medical Ethics,* 5th ed., Davis Company, Philadelphia, 1961.

It seems very strange that the men who apparently are so horrified at the thought of any interference with the processes of nature now proceed to turn around and recommend the rhythm method as a way out of the dilemma. Are they not inconsistent when they condemn birth control as the immoral and willful setting aside of God's will and command, since it "frustrates God's one purpose of sex and marriage," yet in the same breath sanction exactly what they have condemned by merely changing the label? If the one and only purpose of marriage and sexual intercourse is the procreation of offspring, then the rhythm method is as much an interference with that purpose as any other method. Its very purpose is to prevent conception, and it is recommended and carried out with such great care for just that. Birth control remains birth control, even though the name is changed. Not the means but the end intended makes an act like this moral or immoral.

Because of the attitude of the Roman Catholic Church, its power and prestige, sterilization has become a very controversial subject, and discussions concerning it are frequently on the plane of emotion and prejudice rather than logic and guidance of the Spirit of God. We should remember that the fear of the Lord is the beginning (ultimate source) of wisdom, also in matters of sex and procreation. Let our God-influenced and God-directed *conscience* be our guide.

In the first chapter of Genesis, where God tells Adam and Eve to be fruitful and multiply, He is also saying the same thing to the fish of the sea and the fowl of the air (verses 22 and 28). When God speaks to Noah after the Flood (Gen. 9:1), He is giving not a law but a blessing and a promise of offspring. Today, with the longevity and overpopulation problems, the situation is entirely different from those remote times when there were only a few people on earth.

In order to make a proper decision regarding sterilization a person must first become acquainted with all the facts that a competent medical specialist can furnish. Then (and most important of all) the person involved must act according to the will of God. To find that will he must study God's Word and pray for the enlightening influence of God's Spirit, until his mind and conscience are fully clear in the matter.

We all appreciate that children are a blessing and a precious gift from our Creator and Lord. However, in bestowing these blessings and gifts the Lord does not act directly and alone; He co-operates with the parents in His creative work. They are the agents through whom these blessings are made possible. They share in the process as free agents and are therefore responsible. Human parents are not blind instruments in the hands of God as animals are. God endowed parents with reason, judgment, a sense of responsibility, and a will. All of these elevate man far above the animal, which is governed by instinct. All of these make it possible for man to direct the affairs of his own life and to select from the good things and blessings that God has provided, fitting them into his own condition and circumstances.

Besides, we are to consider the effects of sin. Because sin has come into the world not all good things intended by God for man continue to be blessings. Such a great blessing as rain, for instance, can become little short of a curse when it falls at the wrong time or too abundantly. The same holds true of children. In the absence of sin, children, no matter how numerous, would always be a blessing. But sin, with its deadly effect upon the mind and body of man and upon the world in which he lives, has changed that situation. Children, under certain circumstances, may even become an affliction for both the parents and themselves.

Much has been made by those opposed to sterilization of the law of nature. The law of nature is the force by which this universe with all its creatures is sustained and controlled. Man is also subject to this law and will destroy himself if he ignores it. But man's relation to nature is different from that of other creatures. God gave man dominion over all things (Gen. 1:26–28), and this included the power to control and modify nature to his own advantage and for his own interest (Ps. 8:3–6). In fact, the history of man is a record of his taking possession of the world and subduing nature for his own interest. Man's triumph over many sicknesses and his success in prolonging life are excellent cases in point. Another is the use of anesthesia to relieve pain in childbirth or in surgery. No theologian, no denominational resolution, has declared such "interferences" to be a violation of the moral law, of God's law.

Scripture has no clear-cut, definite passages on which an absolute rule of law can be established regarding sterilization, or by which the conscience of the Christian can be bound. But man was given dominion over nature. He is subject to the law of nature and also, to an extent and at the same time, nature's lord and master. He has been authorized to control and modify nature, within certain limits, to his own best interest, and nothing in Scripture prevents him from applying this privilege and authority to the law of nature that governs his reproductive functions. Scripture nowhere prescribes the number of children parents must bring into the world in order to conform to the will of God. Man is a free agent, endowed with intelligence and capable of weighing the consequences of his own action and conduct and deciding whether or not he acts in accordance with God's will.

The animal is forced to mate at certain periods of its life. It must perpetuate its kind at definite intervals according to an unalterable law fixed into its being, and even the number of its offspring is determined by the same law. But man is not subject to that kind of law. He is an intelligent, rational being. It is not reasonable or in keeping with the nature and purpose of man to leave a matter of such tremendous importance as parenthood to chance, accident, or the unguided blind process of nature.

Parenthood implies responsibility for the physical, mental, moral, and spiritual care of all offspring, and that over a long period of time. It also involves consideration for the physical, mental, and moral *health* of both the father and the mother. Let us quote the Apostle Paul in Phillips' new translation: "Do not cheat each other of normal sexual intercourse, unless of course you both decide to abstain temporarily to make special opportunity for fasting and prayer. But afterward you should resume relations as before, or you will expose yourselves to the obvious temptation of the devil." (I Cor. 7:5)

Finally, we would say that birth control, either temporary or permanent (sterilization), belongs to the realm of Christian liberty. A true Christian is "ingrafted into Christ," according to Scripture, and the Spirit of Christ guides him. He is not bound to a set of rules, precepts, prohibitions, and injunctions—unless he finds them expressly stated, as Divine directions, in the Divine Word—the Bible. And, as we have seen, there is no such direction concerning sterilization in the entire Bible, from Genesis to Revelation.

But Christians realize that their liberty is never absolute —it never means irresponsible license. The conscientious man and woman will always exercise their liberty with the fact in mind that their lives, including the sexual and procreative functions, belong to God.

There is nothing wrong or base in lawful and continued sexual relationship, under varied physical conditions, when viewed in that light. Rather, it is a boon from Heaven and can make for mutual contentment and happiness.

PART IV

NATURAL CHILDBIRTH

EDITOR'S NOTE

The term "natural childbirth" was first used in 1933 by an English obstetrician, Dr. Grantly Dick Read. The entire idea covered by this term is of recent origin; it was developed during the last forty years, and Russian scientists seem to have been the ultimate originators. From Russia the idea and its practice were carried over into England and France, and from there, in late years, "natural childbirth" found its way into the United States. Both here and in Europe the natural childbirth method is fast gaining ground, though no exact statistics are available at this time. The numerous obstetricians who favor the method seem to be "thoroughly sold on it," and many of them preach it with an evangelical ardor.

The practitioners of natural childbirth describe it as a program of prenatal preparation by the pregnant mother. The mother usually attends classes together with other expectant mothers for exercises in muscle relaxation and for detailed instruction in confinement experiences. Fear is largely eliminated; she labors in full consciousness, with a minimum of drugs; whatever pain occurs she bears with courage; the whole experience, instead of being gone through like an insensate, feelingless lump of flesh, brings her closer to the God of life and to the tiny, precious infant that she has just expelled, consciously, purposefully, bravely, and, regardless of discomfort, *happily,* from her own body. The effect, so it is said, is *lifelong.*

15

CERTAIN DISTINCT ADVANTAGES
OF NATURAL CHILDBIRTH

Ross L. Willows

Dr. Willows, a **Protestant**, is a Specialist in Obstetrics and Gynecology in Winnipeg, Manitoba, Canada.

The history of childbirth spans the history of man. The scientist examines this process and cannot but be amazed at the intricate steps as nature retraces the path of creation and produces a new and living child.

But it is not the process, or processes, that are our central interest. Rather it is the attitudes of men toward these processes which we wish to examine. In these attitudes we can see many changes. The changes have come about as ignorance and superstition have been replaced by knowledge and confidence.

How did the primitive mother face childbirth? She had available, as the mother of today, the account which other women gave to her of what happens on the great occasion. Some of this would pertain to the difficulties that existed and the pain that had to be endured. Too often it was this part of the experience that was enlarged on with considerable feeling. To balance this there was the fatalistic acceptance, which, coupled with a strong maternal drive, made this experience a much coveted one. The only way that the primitive woman could achieve her highest role in her society was through childbirth. Then, of course, the results helped to blot out some of the darker moments of her experience.

Little assistance was available to the early mother. The more experienced women gradually assumed the role of midwife. They stood by to render what assistance experience and instinct allowed them to provide. This consisted of the cutting of the cord, attendance on the baby for the first critical minutes, sometimes an effort at delivery of the placenta and control of bleeding in the final stages.

The Bible makes a definite reference to the childbearing function. In Genesis we read how our ancestral parents were banished from the idyllic innocence of Eden to the stern realities and exposures of life in contest with nature. Unto the man the pronouncement was that "cursed is the ground for thy sake, in sorrow shalt thou eat of it all the days of thy life." Unto the man was committed the role of *self-preservation*. To the woman came this edict: "In sorrow thou shalt bring forth children." To the woman was committed the role of *race-preservation*. Experience has taught us the truth of these words. Yet it is from these two basic activities that we derive some of the fundamental satisfactions of living. Sorrow and joy have commingled.

The activity of midwives is recognized in the Bible. One attended Tamar as she gave birth to twins (Gen. 38:28). In the sojourn in Egypt it was the midwives who were ordered to destroy all the male Israelite children.

The most significant changes in childbirth have occurred in the last century and a half. Out of desperation delivery by Caesarean section[1] was undertaken. This was a step forward

[1] "Caesarean section" means the delivery of a baby by a route different from the usual one. When the natural passageway is obstructed, or other conditions make it desirable or necessary, the abdomen, and then the uterus, are opened for the birth of the child. The term has been derived from the name of Julius Caesar, who, it is said, was born by way of such a surgical operation. —EDITOR.

despite the fearful mortality. Slowly, along with advances in other departments of medical science, milestones were passed: the conquest of childbed fever, the introduction of obstetrical forceps, the application of ether and chloroform,[2] the introduction of blood transfusions, and the discovery of antibiotics. All this has served to diminish the maternal mortality by one hundred times—from five out of every 100 to five out of every 10,000.

One of the real contributions of the Western world has been in the realm of prenatal care. Prevention has been specially emphasized. The patient is assessed early and a complete health check is undertaken. The onset of significant complications is met early and adequate precautions are taken. So successful has this program become that it is estimated that a woman in the pregnant state suffers a lower mortality for this period than the nonpregnant woman as a result of the close observation that she receives.

Ninety per cent of pregnancies fall into the category that would be regarded as normal. A normal pregnancy occurs when after approximately forty weeks a mother goes into labor with her infant's head directed into the birth canal. The contractions of the uterus increase in intensity until the mouth of the uterus is opened and the infant is delivered through the dilated birth canal. The time consumed for this depends on the strength of the contractions, the size of the infant, and the capacity of the birth canal to accommodate the baby. The process means the investment of some energy and may be accompanied by considerable discomfort. This

[2] Ether and chloroform are anesthetics that were widely used in the former century and in the beginning of the present one to take the edge off the pains of childbirth or to numb the sensory nerves altogether. In this modern day ether and chloroform are still being used for these purposes, to an extent, but other analgesics and anesthetics such as demerol, nitrous oxide gas, ethylene, and cyclopropane have largely taken their place. There is also "block anesthesia," by which anesthesia can be localized while the patient remains fully conscious. —EDITOR.

seems to be much more excruciating at the time than after the whole process has been completed.

Much has been done not only to make this experience a safe one but also a more comfortable one. James Young Simpson of Edinburgh was a pioneer in introducing pain relief during childbirth. The proposal that there should be medication to reduce pain stirred up a storm of ecclesiastical protest. Wasn't pain the ordained lot of women passing through childbirth, and wasn't there the Biblical quotation to prove it? However, Simpson was not lacking in practical knowledge of the Bible, having memorized many chapters as a child and having maintained a continuing interest. He was able to refute all arguments both with Scripture and by practical application.

A critic in Dublin wrote that he did not think anyone in Dublin had as yet used anesthetics in midwifery; that the feeling was very strong against its use in ordinary cases, merely to avert the ordinary amount of pain, which the Almighty had seen fit—and most wisely, no doubt—to allot to natural labor; and in this feeling he—the writer—most heartily concurred.

To this Simpson replied: "I do not believe that anyone in Dublin has as yet used a carriage in locomotion; the feeling is very strong against its use in ordinary progression, merely to avert the ordinary amount of fatigue, which the Almighty has seen fit—and most wisely, no doubt—to allot to natural walking; and in this feeling I most heartily concur."

Simpson was the author of a famous pamphlet entitled, "Answer to the Religious Objections Advanced Against the Employment of Anesthetic Agents in Midwifery and Surgery." At its head the pamphlet carried the following texts: "For every creature of God is good, and nothing to be refused, if it be received with thanksgiving." (I Tim. 4:4) "Therefore to him that knoweth to do good, and doeth it not, to him it is sin." (Jas. 4:17)

This controversy was silenced after six years when Queen

Victoria elected to have chloroform for her confinement and testified to the efficacy of this agent. Sir James Simpson was greatly honored in Edinburgh and became the honorary superintendent of Clubber's Close, the mission founded by Dwight L. Moody.

There have been changes since the first introduction of anesthesia. Many agents have been tried but only a few are now still preserved for the relief of pain in childbirth. These fall into three classes: those that produce relaxation, those that relieve pain, and those that produce complete anesthesia.

It is well recognized that the patient will progress more satisfactorily when she is relaxed. For many this is difficult for various reasons. Some women are habitually tense, some are tense because of a new environment, some are tense because of fear. Having enabled the patient to relax, then we are concerned with the relief of pain. We are aware that thresholds for pain show wide differences from patient to patient. The ordinary way of dealing with this pain is to administer an analgesic drug. This is limited to the amount that will ease pain without depressing labor or the infant. As labor reaches its climax we may wish to give complete anesthesia. This will block out all pain and may mean that the patient will be asleep when her baby is born.

Natural Childbirth

I should like to examine how natural childbirth may alter this plan of management. Not all doctors who favor natural childbirth have the same conception of it. Some wish to use this method only in a *minimum* degree. They wish to preserve the natural functions of childbirth as much as possible and use only those scientific additions to the process of childbirth that sustain and ease the natural functions. They wish to keep the benefits of participation by the patient in the birth process. Other doctors believe in a *maximum* application of natural childbirth. This would imply a total rejection of drugs for the relief of pain, and no deviation whatsoever from the natural process of labor.

For the patient who elects to follow a program of natural childbirth, her experience would be directed along the following principles: First she would be asked to take a period of instruction. The general pattern is for her to be enrolled in prenatal classes, usually under the instruction of a nurse who has been especially trained in this field. Information about such classes—place where, time when, method of enrollment —can be readily obtained, through the information desk, from the secretary of the medical office of any fair-sized modern hospital. The number of cities and towns in which such classes are being conducted is constantly growing. These classes are very important since they give the prospective mother the background of information which permits her to meet each new development of her pregnancy with some anticipation and confidence. These classes pass on information dealing with anatomy and the physiology of pregnancy. There is a description of the various steps of labor and what she may expect as she passes through each phase of her labor. They also teach the patient various means of relaxation so that the problem of tension may be removed. The usual method is to teach the patient to concentrate on deep breathing as an aid to relaxation of all her muscles. Another aid is the use of hypnosis. This really means that relaxation is carried further by means of suggestion. Some patients become very proficient at this and give an outstanding performance as to the ease and efficiency of delivering a baby.

Having fully absorbed the knowledge of the classes, the patient is now ready to undertake the delivery of her baby. The striking thing in these patients is the calm and confidence that they present during the course of their labor. They will often confuse those that are observing the first stage of labor since they are progressing without the usual signs of discomfort. Does the patient have less discomfort because she is experiencing "natural" childbirth? Complete relaxation tends to diminish discomfort. However, the chief factor is that she is adopting a new attitude toward her discomfort. Rather than experiencing panic as to what the experience is going to do to her, she accepts the discomfort and devotes her attention to complete co-operation in delivering her baby.

There are some limitations in the achievement of *complete* success in natural childbirth. The first is with reference to the make-up of the patient and her degree of desire. Not every patient can apply herself sufficiently to the method or achieve a mental state adequate to undertake the work and to ignore the associated discomfort. Pain thresholds vary from individual to individual. Those with a more stoic approach find little difficulty in ignoring the inevitable discomforts in childbirth. On the other hand, some individuals are more sensitive and every nerve stimulation registers most exquisitely. The patient may find that her preparation was inadequate for the needs of her particular experience. In such a case help should be available. That help must consist of the ordinary modern anesthetic or sedative drugs, or both, administered by the obstetrician in charge, accompanied perhaps by a drug that eases and accelerates the birth process. In accepting such help it is unfortunate if it should be accompanied by an overwhelming feeling of defeat or guilt. It should be accepted that only a certain group of individuals may rely on the training of natural childbirth for *complete* support in their labor. Every candidate should be prepared to accept whatever help is needed.

Another difficulty is that the forces of nature do not always succeed in achieving their objective. Accidents may occur along the way. Labor may become obstructed. The infant may be in distress. There may be excessive bleeding. To benefit from the advances of science there must be careful observation by an experienced physician. In 25 per cent of the cases some special contribution is required for the increased safety of the mother and infant. The importance of the team effort cannot be ignored.

It would seem from this discussion that there are two courses that may be followed in the conduct of labor and the management of the pregnancy that precedes it. One emphasizes the application of all the scientific advances that have been made to date. The other course admits scientific assistance only when it is absolutely necessary, preferring to effect delivery of the baby by the natural powers alone. We know that excesses have been perpetrated along both courses.

The temptation to rely on the newer scientific aids has led to some abuses. The induction of labor by infusion of a pitocin solution or by artificial rupture of the membranes may be of great service to the mother. But to follow such procedures as a matter of convenience is inadvisable. The complications are too great. The Caesarean section appeals as an easy short cut around some of the difficulties and discomforts of labor, but it is not without its complications and dangers. There are certain recognized standards for the operative maneuvers in the use of obstetrical forceps. When these are ignored trouble may ensue.

Likewise, the dedicated devotee of natural childbirth deserves a word of caution. There are limitations to this method. It is disconcerting to receive the responsibility of an exhausted mother who finds herself unable to achieve her goal of natural childbirth. As in every aspect of life, the scientific and the natural approach should go forward hand in hand. We may reap the benefits of the discoveries in both fields as we explore the riches of the experiences that nature has to offer us while science makes it safe.

"Doctor, what do you think of natural childbirth?" We hear this question rather frequently. Especially when we encounter a mother who sees in her pregnancy a unique experience and who wishes to keep spiritual values foremost. My reply is one of encouragement and of caution. A Christian's faith particularly fits her to reap the greatest benefits from the experience of natural childbirth. Faith is the answer to anxiety and fear. So it becomes a Christian to undertake her pregnancy in a confident manner. In her life all things are committed unto her God, so in this particular undertaking, which is a climax to her marriage, she may achieve greater spiritual dimensions as she commits herself unto Him. I have watched as the patient passed each new milestone. I have observed the courage with which she faces the delivery of the baby. There seems to be a real reward as she hears the baby's first cry and experiences the flood of well-being "in the joy that a child is born." Childbirth has a great potential for those who are ready to develop and grow through it. It is also good to have the steady hand and the extensive knowledge of the experienced physician in the background, ready to give assistance when a shadow falls across the path or when the flesh falters as it strives to reach the goal.

I commend the experience of natural childbirth, not as an enthusiast but as an advocate. To some it has meant a great deal and for everyone it can yield something. Certainly, we should take God into this experience as into every experience of our lives. In so doing the new mother can make childbirth an experience that will yield unto her a richer faith and a greater joy.

16

NATURAL CHILDBIRTH IS
PREPARED CHILDBIRTH
JOHN R. WATSON

> **Dr. Watson** is a Specialist in Obstetrics and Gyne-
> cology. He is of the **Protestant** faith, and prac-
> tices in Medford, Oregon.

The basic tenet of my faith is that human life
exists because man was created by God. Moreover, human
life will continue to exist as long as God wills it. Each new
life that is born is as much a miracle of God's creation as the
initial origin of life itself. The simple birth of a baby, when
scientifically studied from conception to fruition, becomes an
extremely profound process which the mature individual
comes to regard with great awe. Reduced to basic fundamentals, it takes a good ovum, a good spermatozoon, and the will
of God to create an infant. Stated more simply, each new life
is a gift from God, and it ought to be regarded as such by
everybody.

Fundamentally, "prepared" childbirth connotes merely the
development of an expectant mother's understanding of, and
faith in, God's process of childbirth. From the beginning of
recorded time fear has been the worst part of the whole process. Knowledge dispels fear. Young women need to be assured that they are wondrously designed by the Creator for
the purpose of childbearing, and that all human beings on
the face of the earth have gone through the birth process.
The obstetrician must care for his maternity patient's physical

health by all modern means and necessary medicines; he must assess their physical childbearing capacities with wisdom and accuracy; but his task is not completed until he has considered the mental, emotional, and spiritual attitudes of his maternity patients.

The mother who looks upon her expected confinement as the fulfillment of God's will in her life is not likely to be overwhelmed by dread or fear as she approaches her time of labor. The woman who deeply loves her husband will desire to fulfill their mutual love by giving birth to the expected baby. Such a woman can view the discomforts of labor as small compared to the sacred joy of giving birth to a new life. Conversely, the woman who has little concept of God and looks upon her pregnancy as an unfortunate incident or accident may be expected to view the childbearing process with dread, alarm, and misgivings. These two examples illustrate how mental attitudes have a direct bearing on the experience of labor. In actual practice maternity patients run the gamut between these two extremes in countless variations.

How then can maternity patients develop the proper attitude toward childbirth? At the beginning we should consider not just the expectant mother, but we should encourage the concept of "the expectant family." The husband and wife who jointly contemplate the birth of their child can share this experience with keen anticipation. Through the use of pamphlets, books, movies, and lectures both husband and wife should be educated to understand as clearly as possible the entire process, from conception, through growth and development of the infant within the womb, up to and including the mechanics of labor and delivery.

At this point we might ask: How does this concept of "prepared childbirth" differ from so-called "natural childbirth," as propounded by the late Grantly Dick Read? Unfortunately some enthusiastic exponents of "natural childbirth" have misconstrued Read's original premise to the extent that most people think the term synonymous with "painless childbirth." The misguided implication that "natural childbirth" is "painless childbirth" has caused a great number of mothers to be wholly disillusioned and to consider "natural childbirth" a fraud. In fairness to Dr. Read, it should be pointed out that he actually taught a valid concept, namely, that the pain of labor is intensified by the tensions resulting from fear.

Of those who investigate the books on "natural childbirth" about 10 per cent want no part of it; about 10 per cent who follow through the instructions think it works almost perfectly; about 40 per cent conclude that it is hokum; and about 40 per cent feel that it gave them help in going through labor and delivery, even though they accepted pain medications and anesthesia. From these statistics it is apparent that "natural childbirth" will not be helpful to at least half of the maternity patients, and will be only partially helpful to another 40 per cent. Any method that achieves a successful application rate of less than 50 per cent will not apply to the needs of the majority of obstetrical patients. However, the most prevalent objection to this method is that it deprives many mothers of the benefits of scientific advances that have been achieved in modern obstetrics, such as judicious medical pain relief, the shortening of labor by the intelligent use of forceps, anesthesia at the actual time of delivery, and the prevention of damage to the maternal muscles which regulate the function of the bladder and rectum by employing episiotomy[1] measures. It does not seem wise to many to relegate all patients to the type of deliveries performed by midwives in the Middle Ages. This writer believes in natural childbirth in the sense of "prepared childbirth," which means the intelligent use of obstetrical knowledge applied to mothers who are prepared for the experience, physically, mentally, emotionally, and spiritually.

[1] Incision of the external genital organs during childbirth to avoid undue laceration. —EDITOR.

The Bible says, "In sorrow thou shalt bring forth children." (Gen. 3:16) When chloroform and ether were discovered in the 1840s many people felt that pain relief during childbirth was contrary to God's will. But the same Bible tells us that God caused a deep sleep to fall upon Adam before He extracted a rib from which Eve was fashioned. If a Biblical excuse is necessary in order to recommend anesthesia for delivering a newborn child, this verse might be considered. Besides, there is Jesus himself going about doing good and relieving suffering, and picturing the Day of days on which those who have bestowed physical benefits upon His own will be highly rewarded (Matt. 25:31, etc.). There is also the general trend of the entire New Testament and of the Church in its onward march through the ages—a trend toward alleviation of physical suffering and amelioration of human distresses. There certainly is enough authority to alleviate as much of the pain of childbearing as possible, without jeopardizing the mother's health or the newborn infant's ability to traverse the birth canal safely. It is not a disgrace to womanhood that mothers acknowledge some pain in the process of childbearing; rather, it is cruel to withhold from parturient woman pain-relieving measures when these measures can be wisely and safely employed.

Patients often ask how one can explain miscarriages, fatal monstrosities, and stillbirths in the light of God's love. For the most part, I believe that spontaneous miscarriages are God's way of eliminating defective and faulty conceptions. They represent blessings in disguise. How much better it is to cast off a defective pregnancy than to give birth to a defective child! The fact that nearly 98 per cent of all babies are normal is more astonishing than the realization that some 2 per cent of the babies are born with one or more congenital abnormalities. As to stillborn infants or fatal monstrosities, we have no general, satisfactory explanations for them. But I am convinced that these are not the intentional result of God's wrath or punishment, as some people have believed, or possibly still believe. It is inconsistent with my concept of God's love that He would deliberately create a monstrous helpless infant to punish an evil parent. I cannot conceive that God would cause one human being to suffer in order to punish another.

Let us all acknowledge that our understanding of God and His creative power is very, very incomplete. We cannot possibly comprehend how He accomplishes the miracle of human life. As for myself, though I cannot comprehend the mystery of the creation of life, that part which I do understand is so awe-inspiring that I have complete faith in God, the eternal Source of life and its almighty Creator.

17

THE ADVANTAGES OF FULL CONSCIOUSNESS IN CHILDBIRTH

William H. Hazlett

> **Dr. Hazlett** is a Specialist in Natural Childbirth, Obstetrics and Gynecology. He is of the **Protestant** faith, and lives in Wyoming, Pennsylvania.

With pain a part of the human condition, concern joined two people together. When the first woman in labor was comforted, natural birth, as the animal knows it, ended. Man expected better than nature's chance results. Concern and comfort during labor proved beneficial. With the means remembered, obstetrics was born.

The invention of the obstetrical forceps, the refinement of surgery, and the discovery of anesthesia established obstetrics as one of the sciences and the obstetrician as the woman's logical attendant.

For his services she gambled a precious possession—her human consciousness. At the time, the feminists were on the rampage. Their lofty aims of equality with the male, social and otherwise, concealed bitter disdain for woman's natural function as sexual partner and childbearer, and her domestic role as wife and mother. They concentrated on the pain of labor as proof of woman's deplorable condition.

The obstetrician struggled with his two adversaries—the midwife and the grim problems of pregnancy and parturition (childbirth). By-passing the former, he consolidated his knowledge in female anatomy, physiology, pregnancy diseases, and labor complications. But the feminists esteemed him most for his bottle of chloroform. Anesthesia became consecutively a fad, an obstetrician's routine, a woman's right —a custom. And deeper sentiments of the pregnant woman went unexamined. Methods have been refined; new methods developed. An array of drugs, protecting her from the onslaught of pain, provide her with a synthetic nirvana that threatens to separate her from the feminine self which is intended to be unique.

Anesthetic Arsenal

Analgesic drugs reduce pain. Demerol is the most popular. Small doses dull the pains of labor without appreciable distortion of thought and behavior. Of all the drugs now to be considered, demerol is the least offensive in its distortion of consciousness.

One *amnesic* agent, scopolamine, enjoys popularity. When combined with demerol, it provides the modern version of "twilight sleep." Its purpose is the obliteration of labor's memory. It works admirably.

Tranquilizers and *sedatives* are frequently combined with the analgesic drugs or the analgesia-amnesic ("twilight sleep") mixture. The tranquilizers (phenergan is an example) potentiate the effect of the analgesic drug and moderate the excitatory action characteristic of scopolamine. When the tranquilizer is used with demerol, the analgesic action of the latter is enhanced. A mild depersonalization and amnesia result. Women seeking acuity of consciousness find this objectionable. The most popular sedative is seconal. Its double purpose is to induce somnolence and to strengthen the amnesic effect of scopolamine.

The preceding drugs are employed during the dilatation of the uterine cervix—the first stage of labor. The *anesthetic* drugs are usually employed during the second stage of labor as the uterus propels the fetus into and through the birth canal. These *anesthetic* drugs are divided into two main groups—the *general anesthetics* and the *conduction anesthetics*.

Demerol distorts acuity of consciousness minimally; phenergan, combined with demerol, more so; scopolamine, markedly. *General anesthetics* extinguish consciousness; ether, chloroform, and nitrous oxide are examples.

Other than local anesthesia and pudendal block, which numb only the vulva and the lower vagina, the popular *conduction anesthetics* are caudal, "saddle block," and epidural —the spinal anesthetics. From approximately the waist down, sensation is obliterated. Temporary muscle paralysis, from the same level, is partial or complete. The uterus continues to contract, completing the dilatation of the cervix and the descent of the fetus, at least to the point where forceps can be used to extract it. The woman remains unaware of her organic accomplishment, except second hand from her attendants. If the amnesic, tranquilizing, and sedative drugs are withheld and her sensorium (sensory apparatus) remains clear, she finds herself detached from those parts which are accomplishing her creative purpose. And with these parts detached from her person (so far as sensibility and physical action are concerned) she perceives, knows, and learns nothing.

General anesthetics extinguish consciousness; *conduction anesthetics* dulcify consciousness by dissociating womanly *becoming* from feminine *being*. Acute consciousness is categorically different. Mind and all of the body are intact. The woman is acutely aware of herself, her body, and her fetus. She pays little heed to her surroundings. The irresistible intermittent urge, initiated by the contractions of the uterine muscle, causes her, with a full breath of air, to grasp with her hands whatever is available for support. Her neck muscles strain, neck veins distend, and face grimaces. She pulls with her arms, shoulders, and back. Her vagina and rectum relax and she forces with all of her might. Rather than the uterus in action, it seems that her infant inside forces her to force. In the midst of it all, though the project seems insuperable, despite probability of self-injury and the possibility of self-destruction, her mind, body, and entire being converge on that process of becoming something more than she ever was before.

Toward Higher Consciousness

Scarcely is there a less likely place than the *Kaffeeklatsch* to expect the evolution of higher feminine consciousness. In open-end discussions among two or more young women, the ingredients of the woman's world (sexuality, pregnancy, childbirth, and nurturing of children) are blended, and the subject matter inspires and maintains a continuum of internalized search. In her natural subjectivity she perfuses intuition with conscious ideas. Occasionally a new superstition is born, and a lot of garbage is culled, but inevitably knowledge is increased, understanding is attained, and feminine consciousness grows.

A woman tells her story; another listens. Bits of knowledge are retained. The telling of the tale has a twofold purpose: to inform others and to examine herself. During the latter, she seeks higher consciousness.

No matter how diffuse or superficial the conversation, each participant leaves with a thought or two to dwell upon in solitude and later discussion. Such is woman's search in experience for her place in the creative whole. From the man's viewpoint, feminine confab is a waste of time, but notoriously woman's mind flits about and knowledge accumulates. The content seems trivial simply because, to her, the earth-shaking conclusions imperative in masculine discourse are unnecessary.

Labor and delivery is a frequent topic: her attendants, their methods; her behavior; her perceptions; what her organs and her willful action have done to and for her—what, in short, childbirth means to her.

Comments and opinions vary with the labor phenomenon —and the person: disparagement of labor as cruel, animal-like, and "in this day and age" unnecessarily inelegant; nostalgic comment on an experience treasured; lament for the project ineptly completed; sympathetic comment betraying vicarious re-experience. If there is no nucleus of consciousness in perception and action, or if perception and action are pharmaceutically or operatively distorted, she has no psychophysiologic point from which to initiate her search. If consciousness in perception and action accompanied the creative event, new discoveries and new knowledge—a higher consciousness in the feminine domain—are made and attained.

The concept of higher consciousness through feminine natural function—specifically, in this presentation, pregnancy and childbirth—need not be too perplexing. In the secular world the cultural and intellectual revolution of the past decades, especially among women, provides evidence enough of the search for ultimate truth. Similarly, with implicit faith in the basic tenets of Christianity, all his life the Christian continues to search the Scriptures for ultimate truth. On the premise that the pregnant woman's intuitive closeness with God is authentic, this concept provides a peculiarly feminine pathway to ultimate truth which, because she is human, is impossible to attain, but because she is woman, she seeks. Each step in which understanding is enhanced becomes a higher stratum of consciousness.

During pregnancy she lives intuitively with ultimate truth. Setting out deliberately to find it, she encounters awful gaps in knowledge which confound her mind, such as—

1. Obstetrical science is limited. It is grounded in pathology (tissue disease), yet the causes of pregnancy's most troubling symptoms and some of its most serious complications have no detectable roots in diseased tissues. This is true of one-third of all spontaneous abortions, most premature labors and toxemias, and certain types of abnormal labor.

2. Psycho-physiological (psychosomatic) obstetrics, an off-

shoot of the psychoanalytic theory, is still in its infancy. (No doubt the answer to some of these serious obstetrical problems lies here.) Much has been learned about the mind of the pregnant woman, but to what extent her mind affects the pregnancy, her fetus, and her future—of that little is known.

3. A vast gulf exists between woman's intuition and the objective knowledge of her attendants and entourage. Because her fetus "doesn't move like it did last time," for example, the pregnant woman might sense that "something is wrong." (Acquaintances suggest she needs calcium pills.) The psychologically inclined obstetrician suggests that numerous pertinent conflicts have prompted her disturbing intuition: her early pregnancy surprise, rejection or resentment, the contingent guilt and anxiety, her husband's apparent unconcern, her overconcern for a toddler son or daughter soon to be displaced, a forgotten violent reaction to a baby sibling who long ago displaced herself. If tragedy strikes—a pregnancy or labor complication, a malformed or dead baby—intuition and objectivity have concurred; each has foreseen tragedy. In review, the woman rejects the objective interpretation; the obstetrician disparages the intuitive.

4. Intuition itself is an unmanageable paradox. When right, it is absolute; when wrong, diabolical. It vacillates, it conjures up absurdity. In pregnancy the woman rests in its sublime and transcendent assurance. She senses an inner harmony with God's creative purpose, yet she fails to reconcile its conciliatory effects with her bodily aches and capricious moods. (Should she accept intuitive assurance as authentic, or reject it as a delusion?)

At present she can only ask "Why?" "Why is this pregnancy different?" Sometimes the obstetrician has a ready explanation based upon clinical knowledge. (But of what value is such knowledge?) His explanation is unrelated to the intuitive clue that prompts the question.

Rooting around with the psychoanalyst in her mind's unconscious furnishes many fascinating details but provides neither comfort nor facts that satisfy. In answer to "Why?" she must settle for the truism, "No two pregnancies are alike." But in the midst and wake of creative activity her quest presupposes an intuitive clue and signifies her need to translate that clue into conscious ideation. It follows, then, that her search for clarification and enlightenment contains the hope for a greater understanding and realization of herself and her purpose in existence. (The *Kaffeeklatsch* is principally the voluble conglomerate of numerous silent searches.) The ideas which take form and mature in each woman, richer at pregnancy's end than at conception, richer in subsequent births than in the first, richer in her daughter's pregnancy than in her own—this is what I mean by higher consciousness.

Natural Childbirth Method

In each of the feminine natural functions (menstrual cycles, coitus, pregnancy, labor, suckling), that which she does and feels exquisitely, the woman considers eminently important. It becomes a part of her person. Distortion or obliteration of perception of what she does (or does not do) during the event is similarly assimilated.

Within the framework of modern obstetrics the Natural Childbirth Program provides a hopeful solution for the woman torn between her need for consciousness in the natural crisis of childbirth and her explicit fear of impending pain.

In this country the Natural Childbirth Program is linked with the name of Dr. Grantly Dick Read, the English obstetrician, who coined the term in 1933. In the Soviet Union the Psycho-prophylactic Method, based upon the benefits of hypnosis in childbirth and remarkably similar to the Read Method, had already begun to evolve. The Soviet Method was adopted by the French obstetrician, Dr. Fernand Lamaze. In the past decade or so, through his influence, it found its way to the United States as "painless childbirth."

Dr. Read contended with the problem of pain and the obstetrician's compulsion to attack it bluntly with chemoanesthesia, analgesia, and amnesia. In America, where obstetrical scientists vied with each other to provide a synthetically perfect childbirth—and women were willing, some years passed before he obtained a clinical hearing.

Women in the Soviet Union escaped the effect of this strange union between the feminists and the obstetricians. Expecting spontaneous, conscious delivery, they labored without frills. The Psycho-prophylactic Method was primarily the humanitarian effort to reduce the pain of labor which no woman enjoys. In England and in America women (those caught in the feminist trap) had to rediscover the importance of consciousness—and then to be taught a method that would make labor more tolerable.

Read's apperception of woman—her pregnancy, childbirth, and early nurturing of the infant—was idealistic. To him pregnancy was a sublime state and childbirth a supremely gratifying experience. He rejected labor pain as a necessary component of normal labor. The condemnation of Eve, he argued, not too convincingly, was not to pain or sorrow but to hard work—childbed labor. Fear, introduced by civilization and society's opinion, incited pain by impairing the workings of the uterus and the voluntary pelvic muscles. On these premises he designed his method of prenatal re-education whose purpose was the elimination of fear and, thus, the prevention of pain.

What, in substance, is the natural childbirth method? Although the adherents of each may demur, both the Read method and its Soviet and French counterpart are similar. It is a program of prenatal preparation and labor conduct whereby, with knowledge of her inner workings, through prenatal practice of specified exercises in muscle relaxation and control, fortified by a wholesome relationship with her attendants, the woman labors in full consciousness. With a minimum of drugs she expels her infant from her body.

Does the natural childbirth method abolish pain? Does it reduce pain? An elusive phenomenon, pain is difficult to measure and its measurement provides a poor basis for either exposition or argument. The answers are bound to be unsure, problematic. But too much attention has been paid to the method's ability to relieve pain, too little to its purpose, which is woman's conscious experience of her feminine self.

Implicit in the young woman, profoundly powerful, lurks her purpose in existence—to participate in the continuous creation. Close to nature, she is close to the God of nature. In pregnancy and labor she commits herself wholeheartedly. Acute consciousness contains her hope (as well as her fears). No more than the bloody messiness of the menstrual discharge does she enjoy the pains of labor. She anticipates and accepts them as a part of having a baby. She knows that only a minor portion of human suffering is encountered in the day of labor. With the emptied uterus and the first wails of the infant, procreation rises to merge with creation, and for a while woman touches God. Later, reflectively, she evaluates, criticizes, and judges herself. Nakedly aware of herself as woman, in self-critique she searches in the afterglow for verification of her ephemeral transcendence.

Intellect basks in feminine function, when woman is close to nature and enjoys a progressively resplendent feminine knowledge. But intellect splits off when woman is estranged from nature. It revolts against woman making of natural function a problem demanding the usual solution—the conquest of nature, the man's solution. (Such splitting is occasionally seen in the last weeks of pregnancy when the woman, petulantly waiting, requests that labor be induced. If her request is granted she uses her attendant as the tool of a split-off masculinized intellect.) In her labor she grabs at the scientific miracle that relieves pain, obliterates consciousness, and releases her from the terror that the split-off intellect has inspired. But true feminine intellect remains true to logic and confronts her with the facts of human existence—that in important events acuity of consciousness is more to be desired than oblivion, dullness, darkness, or distortion; that consciousness is infinitely more to be desired than the void. And intuition, inherent in feminine being, reminds her that for consciousness to grow, flower, and radiate, participation in feminine function must be consciously appreciated.

If the pregnant woman is estranged from nature, what is her hope? Here the natural childbirth method has its distinctive value. In alliance with will, her intellect employs feminine channels of natural function (in the case of the pregnant woman, labor and delivery) to initiate and sustain her search for higher consciousness. Against her grain, she makes up her mind to do what the natural woman does naturally—have her baby naturally. Admittedly, self-persuaded intellect is a poor substitute for natural grace. Modern obstetrical refinements sorely tempt her, making her road difficult—sometimes impassable, as when the obstetrician deprecates woman's latent aspirations. If she fails to try, or tries and fails, an alternate route to higher consciousness is the way of the man. His is the spirit's lonely search for knowledge of God. Ever since Adam this, too, has been no picnic.

The woman needs to search for higher consciousness; this she knows. In pregnancy and its aftermath, hers is an internalized spiritual search. With natural function *consciously* experienced and reflectively assimilated into her person, her search may bring unsuspected good for herself and loved ones. In fact, because in creative purpose she possesses intuitive intimacy with God, woman's spirit often breaks through the boundaries of ordinary thought and knowledge, into near-Edenic fields. True, being human, she will fall and forget. But having risen and transcended, she will have much to delight in, and also much to teach her loved ones, provided she recognizes how ineffective, in this sort of teaching, words really are.

18

NATURAL CHILDBIRTH RECOMMENDED—
WITH RESERVATIONS

DAVID L. TABER

> **Dr. Taber,** Specialist in Obstetrics and Gynecology
> in Burlington, Vermont, is a representative of the
> **Evangelical** faith.

Nothing but tears of joy interfere with the
vision of the excited new mother as she catches her first view
of her bloody but beautiful baby. "It was wonderful!" she
exclaims. Months of careful preparation and training have
been rewarded with the culminating joy of both the mother
and the obstetrician—a healthy and sound child.

This is natural childbirth, a form of childbirth in which
the mother, requiring little or no analgesic or anesthesia and
experiencing little discomfort, is fully awake to participate in
the normal delivery of her child.

A normal delivery is really a very simple happening in
which the spontaneous forces of nature and labor bring to
birth a new individual. Modern obstetrics has made tremendous strides in causing this whole process to be a much safer
and more comfortable one than it was just a few decades
ago. The physician who devotes his life to caring for the
female patient is a student of her anatomy and physiology as
well as her emotions. His training covers the broad scope of
general medicine in addition to the more detailed investigation and study of the female reproductive tract.

From the early stages of pregnancy the woman is under the care of her physician, who will probably soon discover whether his patient is a suitable candidate for natural childbirth and whether she desires to have her baby by this method. At the first visit to her doctor the pregnant woman's complete history is taken and she undergoes a thorough physical examination. At least a preliminary idea of her psychological reaction to pregnancy is obtained at this time. It is then, also, that the road to a normal delivery may be clearly demarcated or difficulties may be visualized. Where a normal delivery is anticipated natural childbirth may be the ideal goal.

Obviously, however, not every woman is a suitable candidate for natural childbirth. I heartily recommend natural childbirth to all who may be eligible. But there are those who are not eligible. Mine is a recommendation with reservations. There are women who necessarily must be delivered by one or another operative method. There are many who at best will be tentative candidates for an uncomplicated and spontaneous delivery. Of these there will be a small number who will be physically and psychologically suited to natural childbirth and who will be found anxious to deliver naturally. The many factors which come into play here include previous medical and surgical problems, psychological elements, pelvic mensuration, and many other major and minor factors involved in the over-all evaluation of the patient.

Labor is a complex phenomenon that occurs at a definite time. The onset of labor is presumably related to certain hormonal changes. It may occur very normally several weeks before or after a specified "due date" which is arbitrarily arrived at by the obstetrician.

The stages of labor are generally considered to be three in number. The first stage commences with uterine contractions which produce an opening or dilating of the lower portion of the uterus, the cervix. The second stage commences with full or complete dilatation of the cervix and ends when the baby is delivered. The third stage is completed when the placenta, or afterbirth, is expelled.

The well-prepared candidate for natural childbirth ofttimes experiences a distinct thrill at the onset of labor. The culmination of her months of preparation is at hand. Usually the early contractions will occur at intervals of ten minutes or more. Gradually the frequency increases, and the intensity likewise shows a rise. During this early labor normal activities are encouraged. The house may be tidied up, children arranged for, bags packed, and other arrangements made. As the strength and frequency of the contractions increase hospitalization is desirable. It is most difficult to predict exactly how long the labor of any individual will last. Upon admission to the hospital the usual routine of "prep and enema" will be the accepted ordeal. Following this, the contractions are often accelerated.

We must now face a unique, highly interesting fact. Most women experience some degree of discomfort, others intensely painful spasms, when this amazing process of reproduction nears its culmination. Why? The general run of people would shrug their shoulders to this question; would have no answer. Or they would say: It's always been that way; that's nature's way, apparently.

According to Drs. Eastman and Hellman, among *physiologic* muscular contractions of the human body only the uterine contractions of labor are painful. Again we inquire, Why? These two doctors suggest several possible explanations, including lack of oxygen in the muscle, pressure on the nerves, stretching of the cervix, and pull on the peritoneum (the membrane that lines the cavity of the abdomen).

But don't we have one great underlying reason? In the first book of Scripture the Lord is quoted as saying to disobedient Eve: "I will greatly multiply thy sorrow and thy conception; in sorrow thou shalt bring forth children." (Gen. 3: 16) The physical conditions just mentioned may be simply the means to carry out this Divine edict. Yet the God of justice is also the God of mercy. He has permitted, especially in these modern times, medical scholars and chemical scientists to alleviate the "sorrow" mentioned in Scripture. He has also led such a man as Dr. Grantly Dick Read, English obstetrician, to prepare the medical world for natural childbirth.

Dr. Read has given us a most interesting view of the relationship between fear and emotional upset and the pain mechanism. He felt that the pain experienced in childbirth is either caused or greatly intensified by the psychological state of the woman. Certainly this basic tenet is borne out as we observe the laboring patient. The tense, anxious woman is almost certain to experience greater discomfort than her relaxed and composed companion in labor.

Based on Dr. Read's premises, a careful program of preparation for the expectant mother has been suggested. This is part of the natural childbirth plan. With the objective of eliminating the patient's fear and developing her ability to relax, classes have been arranged in many areas. Here the pregnant women meet and learn relaxing exercises which they are encouraged to practice at home and use during labor. In these classes, moreover, the expectant mothers learn all about the process of labor and birth and baby care. They are also given the opportunity to become familiar with the delivery suite, the nurses, and hospital procedures, in order to reduce their fear of the unknown. Films are shown and question-and-answer periods arranged. Fathers also may attend. Many patients have found these classes very helpful and have obtained confidence through them.

Those women successful in natural childbirth have discovered it a most rewarding and thrilling experience to have such a conscious part in the moment of arrival of the long-awaited child, a moment never to be forgotten, in which the first real bond between mother and child is formed.

How important that this little voyager should be welcomed by his mother! Wonderful that he should be cuddled to her warm and waiting breast! The psychologists tell us that the spark of motherhood is kindled to a fire as the helpless infant suckles at the mother's breast. Who is more helpless than the newborn babe? Who is more responsible for the life of another than the new mother?

It is very natural to inquire whether religion—in our case Christianity—gives preference to one or the other kind of childbirth. The answer is simply that Christians favor the obstetric method that is most beneficial to both mother and child. As stated above, if prospective mothers are eligible I would recommend to them the natural childbirth method. If not, I would follow the best modern way that reason and intelligence dictate. If discomfort is a problem the obvious answer is to relieve it in whatever way is compatible with the best interests of the mother and child. For one woman a small amount of pain-relieving substance may suffice to enable her to go through her labor with a fair comprehension of what's going on about her. In the case of another much more medication, or even complete anesthesia, may be indicated, especially at the climax of labor.

The Christian woman in labor approaches with confidence a sometimes difficult and uncomfortable period, knowing that she can say with the Psalmist, "The Lord is my Shepherd; I shall not want." (Ps. 23:1) She will also remember the words of the Lord Jesus himself: "A woman when she is in travail hath sorrow, because her hour is come: but as soon as she is delivered of the child, she remembereth no more the anguish, for joy that a man is born into the world." (John 16:21) One can read between those lines of the Savior. He expects bravery, a holy optimism, amidst all the hardships of giving birth. And then think of the far more favorable position in which *we* find ourselves than did the women of Jesus' day, thanks to the blessings of modern science!

In their oftentimes trying childbed experiences, let the souls and minds of our mothers seek shelter, warm shelter, with the great Source of Life!

PART V

ARTIFICIAL INSEMINATION

19

IS AN "ARTIFICIAL" CHILD LEGITIMATE?

Oliver J. Steiner

Dr. Steiner, former Captain U. S. Army, M.C. (Obstetrics-Gynecology Department), is now Diplomate of the American Board of Obstetrics and Gynecology in Buffalo, New York. He is a member of the **Baptist Church.**

Some married couples who are unable to have children through natural intercourse seek to satisfy their yearning for a family by turning to artificial insemination. As for myself, I feel this is morally wrong and legally indefensible. There is one exception to the previous statement: at times artificial insemination using semen from the husband is permissible and desirable. This is referred to in the present chapter as "AIH."

The two types of artificial insemination that I feel are wrong are: insemination from an anonymous donor with whom the woman has no contact whatever (AID), and insemination by fluid from the husband and fluid from an anonymous third person—a blend or compound (CAI).

Those physicians who advocate AID and CAI feel that the main justification for the procedure is that it is superior to adoption, for the reason that it obviates many of the drawbacks to adoption, and also because in this way the child is truly a member of the family, seeing the wife is the mother of the child.

I think I am correct in saying that most Christian physicians feel that adoption of normal babies is the solution for the infertile or sterile couple, when the infertility or sterility is due to irremediable physiological conditions. They base their beliefs on the fact that procreation is not the only purpose of marriage. They subscribe pretty much to the idea and purpose of marriage as these have been outlined in a Report to the Lambeth Conference of 1958.[1] In that report the purpose of marriage is described as being threefold. Very briefly stated, this is declared to be the purpose: (1) procreation of children; (2) the fulfillment and completion of the husband and wife in each other; and (3) the establishment of a stable environment within which the deepest truths about human relationships can be expressed and communicated, and children can grow up seeing and learning what mature life is, and should be, really like.

In addition to the Anglican Church certain other Protestant communions are beginning to look into the artificial insemination matter. The United Presbyterian Church, in its General Assembly of May, 1962, has approved insemination from a donor husband, and also, but tentatively, from an anonymous donor. In this last case the assembly quoted the approbative comment of the American Society for the Study of Fertility. Another large communion that is currently studying artificial insemination through an official committee is the United Lutheran Church. In other Churches the matter is pending.

[1] Report of the Committee on the Family in Contemporary Society, delivered in 1958 to the Lambeth Conference and published in *The Lambeth Conference 1958* by The Seabury Press, Greenwich, Conn., in 1959. —The Lambeth Report also has something to say about artificial insemination, namely, "The Christian rightly accepts the help of responsible physicians in making conception possible, where it may be prevented by some physical or emotional abnormality. Artificial insemination by any one other than the husband raises problems of such gravity that the Committee cannot see any possibility of its acceptance by Christian people. The Committee calls attention to the report on Artificial Human Insemination made in 1948 by a Commission appointed by the Archbishop of Canterbury."

The improvement of the human race by selective breeding (eugenics) is definitely not in accord with Christian principles. Such selective breeding is another reason used by the advocates of AID, and they would like to see the practice grow and become widely established. Eventually this would lead—if many of these people had their way—to mass artificial insemination. It is argued that people of superior intellect and physical stature should be chosen as donors. But doesn't this whole scheme reduce the human being to the level of an experimental breeding animal?

As it is, AID has become a coldly scientific procedure. Artificial insemination began with plant and animal life. In fact, it began ages ago: "The ancient Cretes and Assyrians are said to have been familiar with the cross-pollination of plants. Today disease-resistant hybrid corn of greatly increased nutritional value is evidence of the geneticist's craft. The part played by artificial fertilization in fish raising is common knowledge. Artificial insemination has also been used to bridge isolation barriers between gallinaceous species, notably the cross between the turkey and the pheasant. Some dairy herds are now serviced 100 per cent artificially with semen of genetically superior bulls."[2]

More specific medical indications for artificial insemination are: (1) male sterility—partial or complete loss of reproductive power; (2) hereditary disease in the male; (3) severe Rh incompatibility; (4) biologic sterility—those cases where both partners are essentially normal but in which conception does not occur despite the usual measures taken to treat these individuals. In the case of the wife, the following conditions are necessary before any type of artificial insemination is attempted: (1) the pelvic organs must be normal; (2) the Fallopian tubes must be patent (open); (3) ovulation must be normal and occur in a majority of her cycles.

[2] W. T. Pommerenke, Ph.D., M.D., "Artificial Insemination: Genetic and Legal Implications," *Obstetrics and Gynecology*, 9:189, February, 1957.

It is not within the scope of this chapter to discuss the techniques in great detail. In a case of defective coitus (sexual intercourse), or impotence, the wife can be instructed as to the use of a suitable syringe containing her husband's semen (obtained by masturbation or collected in a washed condom). Ordinarily, however, it is the doctor who takes care of the insemination. He has the patient determine the time of ovulation by basal temperatures or the glucose method, and then instructs her to come to his office within one hour after collecting the husband's semen as noted above. The semen is then injected into the cervical canal and the cervix is covered by a cap, left in place for several hours. The semen can also be injected either into the vagina or the cavity of the uterus.

Freezing semen in insulated containers with dry ice has been used as a means of storing normal semen and is proposed by some physicians as a method for establishing banks of frozen donor semen for future use after quick thawing. It has been successful in animal experimentations and is advocated for human beings by eugenicists to continue good breeding stock in the event of a catastrophic disaster affecting a large number of males.

The only Church, so far as I know, that has taken an official stand on artificial insemination is the Roman Catholic Church. According to Dr. Herbert F. Schmitz this Church has declared, "The use of artificial means to enable the natural marital act to be fertile (for example, the cervical spoon) is permitted. No other form of artificial insemination is in accord with the Divine plan for human procreation. Especially objectionable are donor insemination and unnatural methods of obtaining semen."[3]

Speaking of churches and religion—in most countries of the Western world moral and legal rules and practices are based on Christian principles. Still, there are always a number

[3] Quoted by J. P. Greenhill in *Obstetrics,* 12th ed., p. 1049, W. B. Saunders Company, Philadelphia and London, 1960.

of things that are not specifically condemned by law, and that are subjects of much dispute among Christians. Artificial insemination is one of them. There is the question whether or not artificial insemination constitutes adultery and bastardy. Legal interpretations have not been consistent. The commandment, "Thou shalt not commit adultery" (Ex. 20:14), has always been interpreted as referring to sexual intercourse with someone other than one's husband or wife. Christ further interpreted this to include extramarital lust (Matt. 5:27, 28). But in English-speaking countries the question has been brought to court whether children born as the result of AID and CAI are really legitimate. Varying opinions have been rendered, legitimacy having been established in some cases and denied in others. In Switzerland AID is not forbidden, but the husband has the right to question the legitimacy of the child within the legal limit of three months. After this period the legitimacy of the child cannot be denied.

In the United States legitimacy has been favored by public opinion. In most of the states the legitimacy of the child is presumed, as in all legal marriages. Any child born to a husband and wife living together, when the husband is not impotent, is considered legitimate. Impotency is interpreted as sterility and/or inability to copulate.

Adoption of the child conceived as a result of AID or CAI has been proposed as a solution to the problem of bastardy. However, in order for the child to be adopted he must be proved illegitimate, because in most states legitimacy is presumed for all children born in wedlock, as has been previously mentioned. Besides, husband and wife must sign a statement of consent before a witness, giving the physician permission to select an anonymous donor to inseminate the wife, stating that the husband is not impotent and that they are cohabiting as husband and wife. This supposedly, with the presumed legitimacy of the child, obviates the need for adoption.

There are no accurate records of the number of cases in which artificial insemination is performed. The fact that many inseminations are done without taking the supposedly legal steps and precautions, and that adultery is practiced along with attempts at artificial insemination, make any determination of more or less reliable figures even more difficult. It may be expected that as time progresses legislation dealing with this problem will greatly increase. Questions, both moral and legal, are fast multiplying. Some questions in regard to AID and CAI have been answered from precedents in common law. Not all the answers were in keeping with Christian principles.

Dr. W. T. Pommerenke (see footnote 2) has listed a number of the formidable and knotty questions pertaining to artificial insemination, and we have received permission to quote them, as follows:

1. Is the helping of a normal woman to achieve motherhood without her husband's participation, but with her consent, morally defensible?

2. Is the act of artificial insemination properly a medical procedure?

3. If artificial insemination is a medical procedure, should it be governed by laws applying to medical practices generally?

4. If artificial insemination connotes adultery, is the physician who transfers the semen a corespondent or principal or, in fact, an adulterer? Some have regarded him as such, although it would appear silly to so designate a woman physician. Adultery as usually understood denotes an intimate physical relationship, which hardly exists when semen is artificially injected by a third party.

5. If artificial insemination is an illegal act, is instructing the husband so that he may inject the donor's semen also illegal?

6. To what extent may the doctor be held accountable should the child be defective?

7. When he signs the birth certificate, does the physician perjure himself if he attributes paternity to the husband?

8. Does the husband have the right to divorce his wife on the basis of alleged adultery? Need he accept the child by condonation or adoption?

9. Is the child legitimate?

10. May the mother sue the proxy father for support of her child?

11. May the proxy father sue for the custody of this child?

12. If the biologic father later becomes known, may the child sue for the estate of the proxy father?[4]

In view of these many unanswered questions involving the moral and legal aspects of artificial insemination, I feel that Christian physicians cannot recommend this procedure to their patients in cases where donors would be required.

This procedure, of course, is of post-Bible times. In any event, the Scriptures have nothing to say about the subject as such. Still, the spirit and general instruction of the Scriptures are all against AID and CAI and everything related to them. Speaking for myself, as a man of Christian faith, and thinking of the emphasis the Scriptures put on the

[4] In addition to the legal aspects of artificial insemination there are the psychological problems connected with the practice. For these see the following chapter by Dr. Rex L. Rook. —EDITOR.

sanctity of marriage, the high symbolic meaning of the marriage tie, and the indissolubleness of the family unit, I cannot but place a firm taboo on the whole insemination scheme where donors are involved in one way or another.

HOW WILL A FATHER FEEL ABOUT A CHILD THAT IS NOT HIS OWN?

Rex L. Rook

Dr. Rook, a **Protestant,** is a Specialist in Obstetrics, Gynecology, and Sterility in Westminster, California.

The deepest, strongest, most sensitive emotion in human life is manifested physically as sex and that which is allied with it. The desire to be gratified, the search to find that which gratifies it, the actual gratification itself in the finding and enjoyment of a life partner—all this under normal conditions does not achieve its final end until a child is born. Any tampering with this delicate, yet explosive, emotion and its physical counterparts may cause severe reactions.

Many barren couples are confronted with this problem after examination has proven the wife fertile and the husband sterile. Standing at the fork in the road, the couple see either adoption of an infant foreign to both or the production of a child from the only fertile partner of the marriage through artificial insemination. It is into this dismal set of circumstances that this paper plumbs.

Artificial insemination consists of the introduction of semen (seed) into the genital tract of the female, without sexual intercourse, using either the husband's semen (AIH) or that of a third-party donor (AID). All writers are in accord on one phase of this method of reproduction, namely the emotional part. All agree that the couple must be stable and able to recognize all the psychological ramifications. They must recognize the consequences of a breakdown at any point. The welfare of the child must be given utmost consideration. Many psychological interviews and consultations should be had along with the inseminations, as well as for an indefinite period of time after successful completion. While divorce and suicide are doubled in the childless marriages, and marriage discord is seen less in the sterile couples who desire a child than in those who have no such yearnings, artificial insemination should never be used as a means of saving a marriage from the divorce courts.

Three types of reactions may be listed on the part of the barren woman toward her sterile husband: (1) the aggressive type that insists on a child of her own body and forces consent for insemination from her husband; (2) the accepting variety that will tolerate that particular phase of her husband's inability but requires a material compensation from him—she accepts his material success as proof of his masculinity; and (3) the truly motherly woman who channels her feelings toward other persons or objects, real or symbolic.

The husbands find it easier to turn reproductive impulses in other directions, but inadequacy feelings may follow their inability to satisfy their wives' desires. Donor insemination may play havoc with a family through the husband's jealousy and his resentment of the child. The opposite extreme is the man who accepts the results made possible by an unknown donor and identifies himself as the father. Most men fall somewhere between these two extremes. If the husband's desire to satisfy his wife is transitory, the insecurity results in resentment, hate, hostility, and disgust, which frequently develop gradually over a period of time. If a good, permanent adjustment is made, then success can be shared for all concerned.

Legal complications may prove disturbing. There are practically no laws governing artificial insemination. One could say that science is running ahead of its regulator and refuses to stop and wait for the needed regulations. The courts have not only had relatively few cases, but the decisions have been so variously defined and are even so contradictory that no authority can be attributed to them. As someone has said, the law's response to artificial insemination has been, and will be, perfect horror, skepticism, curiosity, and then acceptance. Where the father is the donor, and the resulting child thereby the biological offspring of both parents, few legal controversies have come up. It is the case of the sterile husband, and the wife with a normal reproductive capacity, and the use of semen from a third party, that sets off the problem.

It has been said by some that in the case of an outside donor furnishing the semen, either the physician or the donor is committing adultery. The child has been conceived outside of the marriage relation, so they say. But others contend that according to all legal statutes adultery is out of the question unless there has been sexual intercourse, and that sexual intercourse, according to all codified law, is a carnal connection between the body of a man and the body of a woman. So, this school insists, adultery is ruled out. We find that, legally, this is hardly a moot question.

Both the husband and the wife must sign a consent for outside donor insemination, the principal reason being that in this way the husband will be unable to charge his wife with infidelity in later years. It should contain a statement of cohabitation, reason for the donor insemination (sterile husband, Rh incompatibility, etc.), permission of freedom and authority for the physician to choose the donor, who must not be identified, and the release of the physician from all responsibility in case of unexpected results. Naturally, right in the beginning stages all this plants the seeds of doubt, suspicion, and mistrust.

The question of legitimacy constitutes the gravest of all the controversial points. It pivots around the innocent party. The child born under these conditions may be held to be illegitimate, if strict interpretation of the legal statutes is made. The school of thought that holds this view is strengthened by the claim that the insemination was artificial, contrary to nature, and thus against public policy. Some have attempted to overcome all the legal entanglements, if not the moral, by adoption of the child, thereby giving legal protection to all concerned.

Included in the serious thought that must be given to this venture is the earnest consideration of the requirements. The donor must be mentally and physically free of disease, be unidentified, have the same Rh status as the wife, have no inheritable or communicable disease, and a semen study that meets the norm. Some people make additional stipulations: the donor must have healthy children of his own, and must be a college graduate.

The husband may be the donor when there is defective deposition of sperm in the vagina. This involves such conditions as extreme obesity, extensive inguinal hernias, hypospadias (congenital opening of the urethra on the underside of the penis), nervous impotence (lack of copulative power due to mental factors), premature ejaculation, and varied malformations. The wife may have a severe vaginitis (infection of the vagina) and revulsion to the sex act.

Besides azospermia (absence of sperm) and severe oligospermia (poor quality as to total count, forms, and motility of the sperm), dysgenic factors (detrimental to the race) and Rh incompatibility are reasons not to utilize the husband's specimen. The husband should not be given the diagnosis of oligospermia until three or four examinations of the seminal fluid have been made at three- or four-week intervals. Fever, fatigue, excessive sexual activity, and loss of sleep can produce a transient finding.

Once the decision has been made to go through the route of artificial insemination toward parenthood, then the study of the time of ovulation is next, followed by a study of the semen. There are many methods available to determine ovulation days, but the basal temperature method is the one most commonly used. Insemination twelve to thirty-six hours before the basal temperature rise is the most successful. As to the semen, that which has an adequate count (above eighty million per cubic centimeter), motility greater than 50 per cent, and morphology of not over one-half abnormal forms, is collected in a sterile container by withdrawal or masturbation (rarely by testicular biopsy). It is kept at a temperature not higher than body heat for not longer than ninety minutes. The specimen should have followed five days of abstinence. Mixing with penicillin G probably will enhance the survival time in the cervical mucus as well as minimize the danger of infection.

There are three methods: the plastic cup—which is by far the most common, the direct method, and the cervical plug.

The plastic cup fits snugly over the cervix or mouth of the womb. To it is attached a tubing that reaches from the cervix through the vagina to the outside of the body. The semen is injected from the syringe into the previously fitted cervical cup. The cup not only provides an anaerobic environment (devoid of oxygen) but also protects the sperm from the vaginal acidity. Continuous contact with the cervix is also possible, as removal does not occur until as much as twenty-four hours later. The cervical cup is inserted in the physician's office, while its removal can be done by the patient.

The direct method is being used less and less, and is being replaced by the cup. The semen is spurted at and about the opening of the cervix with a cool, dry, glass syringe. No attempt is made to introduce the specimen into the cervical canal or the uterine cavity. After the speculum (instrument that holds the vagina open) has been removed, the patient remains lying in the supine position for thirty minutes before resuming her normal activities. Some feel it is best to deposit the ejaculate in the posterior fornix of the vagina (small pocket behind the cervix in the vagina), especially following an alkaline douche. All agree that deposition in the uterine cavity is hazardous, as infection is easily introduced. Good results have been attained by washing and concentrating (centrifuging) the semen.

The third method, the cervical plug, is the least popular and relies on a rubber plug to prevent backflow out of the cervix.

The likelihood of donor insemination being successful is generally reported near 80 per cent (some, however, reporting as low as 50 per cent). The average case requires three to six inseminations over a period of two to four menstrual cycles. When done on days thirteen, fourteen, and fifteen (based on a twenty-eight-day cycle, and counting the first day of menses as day Number One) 50 per cent are successful. Since introduction of the plastic cup, in 1948, there have been no serious complications, while an occasional case of infection was reported following semen insertion in the vagina and cervix. If after three menstrual cycles of insemination conception has not occurred it is best to change donors. With homologous insemination (husband's specimen) the figures of success are highly variable. The reasons for this are the very circumstances that prompted this type of treatment in the first place.

The use of frozen spermatozoa is not too common, but fruitful insemination has resulted from the use of semen frozen up to twenty weeks. Many technical rules have to be adhered to for making this method successful (low temperature of 79° C., treatment with glycerol, slow cooling and thawing, etc.). The results, even though the series of cases is small, seem to be no different from those of any other method.

So far we have dealt largely with the legal and mechanical aspects of artificial insemination. What about the ethics of it? Christian people always relate their ethics to their religion, and to the Holy Book in which they believe the Lord has revealed His wish and will for humanity.

There is no direct information, of course, in Scripture about the practice we are dealing with. That practice originated in modern times; in fact, quite recently. But Scripture does state certain foundation principles about marriage; about the relation between husband and wife that the God of Scripture desires and that He meant for them from the beginning. Marriage is, or should be, an inseparable union. Throughout the entire Holy Book the bringing in of a third party into the very private circle of those whom "God hath joined together" is always accompanied by sinister, ill-omened, disastrous conditions and results.

Ever since Paradise, as the ages rolled along, problems related to marriage cropped up. Moses' Law—such great and far-reaching deterioration had set in, ethically and morally, among mankind—permitted divorce on what we today would call "incompatibility." When Jesus was confronted with the question of the legality and permissibility of the practice allowed by Moses, He at once explained that Moses had tolerated certain things because men of that early age were spiritually and morally incapable of living up to the Divine ideal in marriage; and He then, as God come down to earth, restated the original, basic principle, and directed men to live in accordance with it (Matt. 19:3–9).

Marriage is the supreme expression in human life of *love*. It is a joining together, an interlocking, an enmeshing of two human beings. This applies to all three planes: physical, mental, and spiritual. God planned it that way. Jesus restated God's original plan, "reactivated" it. And the supreme result of that true love-life is the child. Besides, man has been permitted in recent times, through scientific investigation, to detect how very intimate that love-life is, and how rich and marvelous the fruitage. Each partner contributes exactly half toward the essence and constitution of the infant—an equal number of chromosomes (composed of heredity units called "genes") from each. In growing up that infant must be fed a balanced diet of love—love that can only emanate from a unified source of two parts: paternal and maternal. If this ideal is not met or lived up to, only unhappiness and sorrow result.

Now, returning to the ethics of artificial insemination, this writer cannot help but see an inversion of the Divine marriage plan, a contravention of the Divine law, if a third party is invited or bought to take the husband's place in the act of begetting.

At first, in my practice as an obstetrician and a gynecologist, I thought rather favorably of the donor system—only, of course, in case of need. I felt that a real need was being fulfilled. Later, upon closer scrutiny of the whole subject, I decided against the idea. There was the running thought of Scripture. There were also unhappy practical results: man and wife feeling that, essentially, their unity was broken; the fear of bearing an abnormal baby; either spouse now feeling that they could go "stepping out"; or the husband not seeing his wife any longer as a sweetheart but as the mother of a child that was not his own.

Artificial insemination, in my opinion, with the husband as the source of the semen, is allowable when circumstances call for it. The same practice with a stranger as the source is definitely "out."

THE CHILDLESS COUPLE, THE BIBLE, AND THE POWER OF PRAYER

Clarence A. McIntyre, Jr.

Dr. McIntyre, a **Protestant**, Specialist in Obstetrics, Gynecology, and Pediatrics, is a Captain, M.C., at Womack Army Hospital in Fort Bragg, North Carolina.

The attitude of the Christian family and the Christian physician toward artificial insemination should stem, primarily, from an earnest searching of the Scriptures.

There is a latitude of opinion among Christian people about this subject. This does not suggest that the ultimate Author of the Scriptures vacillates. There is but one correct opinion. But Christians of opposing thoughts should humbly admit that "now we see through a glass darkly" (I Cor. 13: 12), and they should remain in true fellowship, regardless.

As to artificial insemination, the term means the introduction of semen into the female reproductive tract by means other than sexual intercourse. The purpose is to produce a pregnancy in a home that is childless. The semen is obtained by masturbation and should be used within one and a half hours unless frozen and stored, according to the technique described by R. G. Bunge.[1] The insemination, to result in pregnancy, should be performed within twenty-four hours after ovulation (the passage of the female sex cell from the ovary into the reproductive organs where fertilization by the sperm or male sex cell may occur).

[1] *Journal of Urology*, 83:192, 193, 1960.

The time of ovulation is determined by following the woman's temperature and examining under the microscope a bit of the lining of the uterus and some mucus from the cervix, the opening of the uterus. The wife should be proven healthy and fertile by examination (passing gases or X-ray-visible dye through the Fallopian tubes and determining that ovulation occurs in the same way after the time of ovulation is found). E. M. Sandler in an excellent article on artificial insemination[2] describes in detail the technique for depositing semen onto the cervix, and recounts also the fascinating historical, legal, and philosophical aspects of the practice.

It is interesting to note that artificial insemination was first used by fourteenth-century Arabs as a weapon in tribal wars. Victory in battle was often dependent on the quality of horse-flesh deployed in cavalry campaigns. At night the combatants would steal into the hostile camp and either obtain semen from superior stallions or inseminate the enemy's mares with semen from inferior stallions. With such a nefarious origin, it is not surprising that artificial insemination has often been considered a questionable practice—aside from other considerations.

The practice among humans falls into two categories, depending on the origin of the semen used. The one category uses semen from the husband, the other from an unknown donor. Let us briefly consider both categories.

Artificial Insemination Using the Husband

For the Christian family and physician, using the husband's semen would appear to be a justifiable practice. Mechanical or anatomical factors occasionally prevent the effective deposition of semen on the cervix by natural sex relations. According to Sandler (see above), artificial insemination to remedy a situation of this kind was first successfully performed in 1790 by Dr. John Hunter, the great surgeon and

[2] *South African Medical Journal*, 34:320–323, April, 1960.

anatomist. Physicians of today are acting properly when they follow Dr. Hunter's example. In fact, they have a far greater exemplar—the Lord Jesus Christ himself. The Gospels are filled with incidents relating the miraculous activity of Jesus in healing and mending people's physical defects, many of them congenital. Physicians therefore are doing the Christlike thing when they use ethical procedures to heal infertility. True, they use means to accomplish their ends, whereas Jesus performed miracles. But Jesus placed the stamp of His approval upon such means as ordinary mortals have to use. Think of the parable of the Good Samaritan who dressed the wounds of the man who had fallen a victim to thieves by "pouring in oil and wine" (Luke 10:34).

Childless couples, however, in asking the doctor to use this means of artificial insemination should insist that the doctor use the husband's semen, not that of a stranger. In the case of a Christian doctor no persuasion on this point will be necessary; the doctor himself will be the first to advise the use of the husband's semen and explain the why and the wherefore.

Though of course the Bible in the primitive times in which it was written makes no mention whatsoever of such a subject as we are now discussing, it gives plenty of "leads" for us to follow in our modern times. Let us mention just two of the outstanding leads, the one primarily in the Old, the other in the New Testament.

In the Old Testament God established His covenant with Abraham (Gen. 17:7 and many other places). God always, in connection with that covenant, mentions the seed-line. For emphasis, in the reference just given He mentions it twice: "And I will establish My covenant between Me and thee and thy seed after thee in their generations for an everlasting covenant, to be a God unto thee, and to thy seed after thee." That seed-line meant a direct, uninterrupted, physical connection with Abraham. The covenant was made effective by the purity of the seed-line. Semen from strangers, if artificial insemination had been practiced in those early times, would have been out of the question. It all expresses the Divine ideal, indicates the Divine will in Israel's procreative life— and Israel was meant to be a model for the nations.

The New Testament "lead" that should be mentioned is the comparison, repeatedly made, of the relation between Christ and the Church with a strictly monogamous marriage. Jesus himself said of the relation of a man and his wife: "And they twain shall be one flesh: so then they are no more twain, but one flesh." (Mark 10:8) Now think, among others, of the well-known Revelation passage: "Let us be glad and rejoice, and give honor to Him: for the marriage of the Lamb is come and His wife hath made herself ready." (Rev. 19:7) If the use of strange semen, as Sandler (see above) suggests, makes a mockery of marriage, would not Christians by this use make a mockery of Christ's relationship to His Church?

Two other matters should be briefly mentioned. As a practicing physician this writer has a great deal to do with the physical side of humanity, but he also relies very heavily on the spiritual. He is a great believer in the power of prayer. A childless husband and wife should do much praying if they genuinely desire a child or children. According to the Apostle James, "The effectual fervent prayer of a righteous man availeth much." (Jas. 5:16) It's something like a farmer sowing his seed. When seed and soil get together we have only the beginning of the growth process. Much can happen of things that lie outside of the farmer's competence. There are such things as excessive heat or cold, drought or rain, the chemical reaction of the soil to atmospheric or weather conditions and its effect, in turn, upon the seed that was sown. The farmer, in other words, needs beneficial action on the part of God. So do the childless husband and wife. But if their continued prayers for a child are not granted it may be that the Lord wants them to employ *special* means. In such a case, and from a viewpoint of the Christian religion, the childless couple are fully permitted to use artificial insemination. And they should keep on praying while they use this special means for they will still need effectual, result-producing blessings from on High.

And now a second matter; a question that should be faced with all frankness. A large group of Christians, the Roman Catholics, under the leadership of their spiritual mentors, object to the use of artificial insemination, even when the husband's semen is used. They assert that masturbation for this purpose is sinful. Paris Souval has succinctly summarized the Catholic and other attitudes on artificial insemination in his article entitled "Artificial Insemination, A Review of Opinions on its Moral Validity."[3]

What about this Catholic argument? As a practical matter of record we might say that the 1948 Kinsey Report (pp. 470, 471) reveals that over three-fourths of adult Catholic males masturbate. That seems to indicate that not all Catholics take their official teachings in this matter seriously. As to Biblical grounds, two principal passages are usually quoted by our Catholic friends. First there is Genesis 38, verse 9: "And Onan knew that the seed should not be his; and it came to pass, when he went in unto his brother's wife, that he spilled it on the ground, lest that he should give seed to his brother. And the thing which he did displeased the Lord; wherefore He slew him also." But this passage does not refer to masturbation; it refers to *interrupted intercourse*. The name "onanism" for masturbation, after the name of the character in this Bible passage, is therefore also wrong.[4] Then there is the New Testament passage. In I Corinthians 6:9 the Apostle Paul says: "Know ye not that the unrighteous shall not inherit the kingdom of God? Be not deceived: neither fornicators, nor idolaters, nor adulterers, nor effeminate, nor abusers of themselves with mankind . . . shall in-

[3] *Medical Arts and Sciences,* 13:119–125; 1959.
[4] Genesis 38:8–10. This Scripture reference has been interpreted variously. See pp. 11, 25, 40 of this book.

herit the kingdom of God." But this passage, also, does not refer to masturbation. It refers to *homosexuality*.

If masturbation in itself, and in all circumstances, were sinful, would not the Bible (which fairly exhausts the list of sexual sins) have made definite mention of so universal a practice? The process of masturbation is no more sinful than any other exercise or physical conditioning associated with growth and maturation.

Donor Insemination

Artificial insemination with semen from a donor has been condemned by most authorities, religious and otherwise. This type of procedure (donor insemination) was first tried out in 1884. Donor insemination is considered in the presence of one of the following situations: a sterile husband, hereditary disease on the husband's side, Rh problem (in the red blood cells), many miscarriages coupled with a high count of abnormal sperm in the husband, and the repeated birth of malformed children. The donor is usually unknown and unrelated to the couple, but of similar race and physique, under forty years of age, married and with at least two healthy children, and free of venereal, psychological, or familial disease. The recipient must be fertile, as previously stated, and of known Rh type. If she is Rh negative, the donor must be also to avoid the familiar Rh problem wherein the baby may be seriously jaundiced.

The donor and his wife as well as the recipient and her husband must sign witnessed consents. They must do so separately to maintain secrecy of identity. The donor and recipient must remain absolutely unknown to one another. Further, the donor must not know whether or not the insemination was successful. Semen banks using frozen stored semen have the disadvantages of expense, tenuous secrecy, and less critical evaluation of the donors. Donor insemination is successful in about half of the cases where the procedure is persistently repeated over a six-month period at times of ovulation.

Is donor insemination adultery? If it were, it would certainly be contraindicated for Christians. However, Christ's definitions of adultery—inordinate lusting after another's wife (Matt. 5:28), or marrying a woman unlawfully divorced (Matt. 5:32), as well as obvious adultery—seem quite remote from the thoughts and actions of all parties involved in donor insemination. Adultery in our country is legally defined as voluntary sexual intercourse between a currently married person and someone of opposite sex other than the spouse. So, this also does not pertain to donor insemination. True, there are some states and countries that define donor insemination as adultery. In such cases Christians will of course obey the Apostle's injunction: "Submit yourselves to every ordinance of man for the Lord's sake." (I Peter 2:13) Nevertheless, donor insemination cannot be definitely equated with adultery, in the opinion of this writer.

There are some uncertainties in Scripture with regard to the status of children that have resulted from unusual or irregular matrimonial arrangements. Many laws and legal writers of our day consider children of donor inseminations illegitimate or bastards. But at once the question arises in what light God viewed the children of polygamous Old Testament families. For example, the patriarchs, the fathers of the twelve tribes of Israel, were the sons of four mothers by Jacob. According to Genesis 30:1–13 and Acts 7:8, two of these mothers were handmaids, apparently not married to Jacob. (It is to be noted in this connection that Christ descended from Judah, after the flesh, and the Israelite priests from Levi, and that both were the sons of Leah, Jacob's first and genuine wife.) Then there was the case of Abraham and Sarah, who doubted God's promise to give them a son and entered a troublesome aside from God's will through polygamy. (Gen. 16:2) Nevertheless, God sent an angel to protect Hagar, the handmaid, and Ishmael, the result of the polygamy. (Gen. 21:17) In fact, God blessed this mother and her son, and some others of the Old Testament progeny of polygamous and extramarital unions. Just as the status of all these children mentioned or referred to is unclear, so the status of the child who is a product of donor insemination is unclear. Donor insemination, however, does seem to be outside the limits of a strictly monogamous marriage so often extolled in Scripture and, as we have seen, held up as a symbol of the holy relationship of Christ and His Church.

Donor insemination is fraught with one frightening possibility—incest. So far no cases have been reported, but the possibility remains. The child who is the product of secret donor insemination might, particularly in a small community, unwittingly marry a child of the donor. This is marriage of siblings, a form of incest. Of incest the Apostle Paul writes, "It is reported commonly that there is fornication among you, and such fornication as is not so much as named among the Gentiles, that one should have his father's wife." (I Cor. 5:1) Of course, the same problem could occur with the adopted child of an unwed mother. That child might unknowingly marry a sibling, a child of the same mother who had later married and had legitimate children. But since all this is hypothetical and no actual cases or litigations have as yet been reported, this argument need perhaps not be pressed too far.

The grounds, as we see it, on which the Christian doctor and family should avoid artificial insemination by an unknown donor are mainly twofold. First, that many Christians are against it and the very serious admonition of the Apostle not to offend or hurt them (I Cor. 8:10–13). Almost unavoidably the donor act would become known, at least among the very close relatives or friends. We all know how it is and goes. A Christian family using this much-questioned procedure might be giving a negative witness.

A second ground is the fact that donor insemination is

unnecessary. The world is full of children in need of adoption. The children meant here are not, usually, those described on the lists of the adoption agencies as physically, mentally, and racially desirable. In our present substandard society prospective adoptive parents usually demand perfection in the child. This is beyond what natural parents are willing to accept. They are willing to "take their chances," or, better, to take what the Lord gives them. The children in real need of adoption are the little Koreans, the racially mixed, the handicapped, the blind, the deaf, and the retarded. We need the spirit that Christ had in mind when He said, "But when thou makest a feast, call the poor, the maimed, the lame, the blind: and thou shalt be blessed; for they cannot recompense thee; for thou shalt be recompensed at the resurrection of the just." (Luke 14:13, 14)

A childless Christian couple who wish to adopt a Korean orphan should consult their clergyman, who can quickly and easily get them on the right track. Those wishing to adopt a racially mixed child should get in touch with a local adoption agency. Those who wish to remove a child from the pathetically inadequate conditions in the State Schools for the Mentally Retarded and place them in a Christian home should see any one of the social workers connected with the State Schools.

The thoughts and suggestions in this chapter are submitted to the readers in all humility. The subject under discussion was somewhat bizarre, and it was delicate. Yet it is fast coming to the fore. It needed handling. We have tried to do so modestly from a viewpoint of medical science. We have also tried to let glints of light fall upon the subject from what all through the ages, by countless millions, has devotedly and reverently been called THE BOOK.

May our small effort be of help to many!

INDEX